Clinton Steele

Clinton Steele is an alter ego. He is a child of 'The Seventies.' At the age of fifty three, he still embraces that era and won't change his ways to conform to modern times. He is an original dinosaur of the seventies and all its values and beliefs. In Clinton's words, the seventies were a time of 'real men.'

Clinton has had a varied and interesting career. His jobs include gravedigger, milkman, film extra, stuntman, stripper, DJ, bodyguard, male escort, martial artist, singer, stand up comedian and now author.

You may have seen his face umpteen times on the big or small screen or heard his velvety tones on the radio or in voiceovers for TV adverts. He has had thousands of walk on and bit parts.

He is a larger than life character and a living legend in some quarters. He is British and proud of it, and is well known for his strong and forthright opinions.

Due to work commitments of a special nature he at present splits his time between living in the UK and the USA.

Kevin O'Hagan

Kevin's main occupation has been as a martial arts/fitness coach for over twenty-five years. He has fought as a professional cage fighter and holds a 7th Dan Masters's grade in Ju Jutsu. He is a well-known and respected face in the UK and world martial arts scene. Kevin has written eight books as well as numerous magazine and website articles on martial arts and fitness.

Kevin first started writing a few fictional short stories in his spare time some three to four years ago and gradually they amounted into a collection. Following a long time ambition, he decided to see if he could get them published mainstream. At present, he has two books of short horror stories published: *A Sting in the Tale* and *A Short Sharp Shock*. Kevin left school with no major qualifications and hasn't had any formal writing training or guidance. He helped create the thoughts of Clinton into words with tongue firmly in cheek.

"Real Men Don't Wear Pink"

A no holds barred guide to resurrecting the extinct '70s male

Clinton Steele
(Assisted by Kevin O'Hagan)

━━━━━━━━━━━━━━━━━━━━━━━━━━━━━

"REAL MEN DON'T WEAR PINK"

A NO HOLDS BARRED GUIDE TO
RESURRECTING THE EXTINCT '70S MALE

Olympia Publishers
London

www.olympiapublishers.com
OLYMPIA PAPERBACK EDITION

A CIP catalogue record for this title is
available from the British Library.

ISBN: 978-1-84897-462-3

(Olympia Publishers is part of Ashwell Publishing Ltd)

This is a work of fiction.
Names, characters, places and incidents originate from the writer's imagination.
Any resemblance to actual persons, living or dead, is purely coincidental.

First Published in 2014

Olympia Publishers
60 Cannon Street
London
EC4N 6NP

Printed in Great Britain

*For my beautiful grandson Logan, may he grow
to be a true man.*

To all my family and friends who have supported my writing.

NOTE

Whilst writing this book we spoke with many people for their views and opinions and researched and sourced numerous websites, books newspaper articles etc., far too many to remember all the sources. We would like to thank each and every one of you for your enlightening thoughts and views.

WARNING...

This book contains strong language, rude, self-opinionated statements and no holds barred views from a real 70's dinosaur. Do not read if you are of a nervous disposition.

Contents

PREFACE

If you have purchased this book, I take it you may well be from the same age bracket as myself.

I was born in the early 60's and my most memorable years growing up were in the Seventies.

I know that every generation will have their favourite time.

Many people older than me will quote the post-war era as a time of great camaraderie and friendship, hope and happiness forged through the sharing of adversary.

Others state that the '50s were magical. The time of rock 'n' roll, Elvis, Teddy Boys and the American culture.

We then have the '60s child: a time of free love, peace, Hendrix, Beatlemania, the Mini Skirt, Mods and Rockers, etc.

I fully appreciate all of this, but for me, the '70s and early '80s bred everything that made it the time of the real man.

It was a time of political incorrectness certainly, but who cared? We hadn't even heard of that terminology then.

It was an era of massive sport and film stars, blockbuster movies, real music, cool toys, great TV, and simple but fun pursuits. It was a time of endless summers, Top of the Pops and Tiswas. A wonderful space in time of Cresta fizzy drinks, space hoppers, platform shoes, flared trousers, Summertime Special on Saturday night television, followed by Starsky and Hutch, Radio One road shows, Proper DJs, Watney Party Seven cans of beer and crisps with the little blue salt bag in the packet.

The '70s were a time of no bullshit, no namby-pamby softness and political red tape, health and safety human rights madness. Life was simple. Men were men, boys were boys. We knew where we stood.

We weren't the emasculated wimps of today who no longer know who they are and how they should behave because society has gone crazy.

If you share my beliefs, then you will be in for a treat in the following pages.

This is a no holds barred, don't fuck with me account of how life was and, in my opinion, should be. I am going to tell it how I see it. I will point out along the way the failings of the modern male, the failings of the country I love and the highs and lows of my decade, the seventies, compared to today.

It's going to get ugly. Be warned!

Helping me put my thoughts and words down on paper is my good old mate, Kevin O'Hagan. He kindly agreed to put my mad ramblings into some sort of order. I owe him a debt of gratitude for that. We go back a long way. We went to different schools together. I got the looks and the brains, he got...? Well, let me think...

Only kidding, he is a top guy. *A true gentleman in a world of fake and false bastards*. A man you would want to be with you in the trenches when the shit was flying.

It is an honour and a privilege to call him my friend and I thank him sincerely for his *relentless* work on this book. Without him, it certainly wouldn't have existed... indeed, neither would I! I am indebted, old buddy, although I still think I can kick your ass!

Anyway, I digress...

So let's get back to how it was and the first step is to categorically state right here and right now: Real Men Don't Wear Pink! Got it?

Clinton Steele, January 2013

The Clinton Steele vision

'I have a dream, a vision, a quest to see the world once again be inhabited with the real male species. Living, breathing specimens of manliness. Tough ,brave individuals not afraid to take on their true male roles. Action men, heroes and role models to all boys out here struggling into manhood. It is my duty to work towards the day when the real man will reappear once more, so that they can forefill the true roles they were born for and destined to have'. Amen.

INTRODUCTION

Remember a time when men were men. We wore lumberjack shirts, ate manly things like giant steaks with no fucking side salad, Yorkie bars, McCoys crisps and Ginsters' pasties. We drank bitter and a whisky chaser or a pint of Blackthorn cider. Lager was the new kid on the block and was viewed with suspicion and, until accepted, came under the heading of 'poofs' beer' or 'that German drink.'

Cocktails? Men drinking brightly coloured drinks with umbrellas sticking out of them in a woman's glass? Not bloody likely. If somebody dared asked back then, "Would you like a cocktail?" the answer was, "Yeah, tell me one!"

When asked as a kid, "What do you want to be when you grow up?" we answered with manly jobs: an astronaut, a policeman, deep sea diver, a footballer or fireman – not a fucking chef, male model, or to be in a boy band!

Discovering your feminine side back then was going into the kitchen to attempt to boil the kettle and look for where the coffee was kept. Safe sex was a padded head board. When you went into hospital to have your tonsils out, you woke up to ice-cream, not MRSA.

A time when wicked meant 'bad' not 'good', when outing meant getting on a coach and going to the seaside for the day and a time when you found an apple, orange and blackberry in your fruit bowl, not at Curry's! I remember Nelson Mandela when he went to prison. Yes, you are looking at a man who remembers a time before retro!

I grew up in a tough era of the '70s where if you carried a comb on you, you were a 'woofter' unless you were going to a football match with the end sharpened to plunge into a rival supporter's ass cheeks!

Being a 'wimp' or 'Nancy boy' was not tolerated and God forbid any boy who confessed he liked listening to music by Donny Osmond or David Cassidy. You basically were a dead man!

We were fucking hard. We liked a drink, a fight and a shag, basically in that order, and normally with fish and chips afterwards. Magic.

But what the fuck has happened to the 'man' of today? Who is he or what is he? Does he even know? Also, what about modern day culture? Film, TV, music, work ethic, etc. etc. It's all gone to the dogs.

Kevin finds that Clinton can get away with a lot more than he can in these days of political correctness, where everybody is afraid to speak their minds.

So he has let Clinton off the leash for this book and let the seventies be relived where life was so more straightforward and simple. *A time that sadly has all but disappeared.*

What the hell would Inspector Jack Regan of the flying squad a.k.a *The Sweeney* say about it all? Probably, "Shut it you slag or I'll break your jaw. Bring back the bleeding '70s!"

CHAPTER 1

Man Up

Where have all the real men gone? They no longer exist. They have lost their identity. They don't know who to be. They don't know what is expected of them anymore. Confused? You bet. Women have messed them up. They have tampered with their hard wiring and something strange has happened to them.

Firstly, you must remember we are male. We are the ones with the balls. Do not forget this. Do not allow yourself to be emasculated. What is all this boy dressing up as girl crap about? Let's put the record straight on this.

Real men don't wear pink!

It just isn't fucking natural. If I had walked into a pub in my teenage years wearing a pink t-shirt, I would have been taken down to the floor like a young wildebeest being attacked by a pride of lions. I would have been severely beaten while being called, "You little Nancy boy bitch," and after reaching the sweet release of unconsciousness, somebody would have pulled my trousers and pants down and inserted the neck of a HP sauce bottle up my rectum to teach me a lesson.

Let's face facts. When you were a baby, you wore blue. *Blue to inform all that looked at you in your pram that you were a boy.* You didn't wear pink. That was for girls. Why now, when you sport a beard, several tattoos and a beer gut that usually constitutes you as a male (there are a few exceptions I have met), do you want to sport girly pink!? Get real. You look stupid. Ditch the pink now!

The modern age has unleashed a new breed of 'man.' You only have to look at the clothes rails in shops like Topman, Burton and H&M. How can you have men's clothes in an XXS size? That size of clothing is either for a ten year old pre-pubescent young girl or some 'stick insect' super model. Not a man.

Some young guys get a kick out of being thinner than their girlfriends and proud that they can wear her eye liner with more panache.

We now have what is termed a *metrosexual*. Gone are the days of chest hair and stubble. Now we have bollock-choking skinny jeans, manbags and moisturisers.

I may be wrong, but even in these days of equality, I feel every female harbours a secret fantasy of being rescued by a knight in shining armour. A man, strong, handsome and rugged that can sweep them up in his powerful arms and whisk them away on a white charger.

What have you got now? A skinny, mincing wimp with a fake tan, shaped eyebrows and a Gucci satchel. *Enough to make real men weep.*

Need convincing, take a certain X-Factor misfit, for example, a long lanky preening poodle. I wish somebody would take him, preferably to the end of a cliff, and push him off!

I still firmly believe a man is the hunter gatherer and is there to look after his lady. He doesn't want to be doing the shopping in Tesco and worrying about whether he should buy Demestos or Toilet Duck or whether to get a 'buy one get one free' on baked fucking beans.

Real men are putting out fires, fighting wars, driving lorries or in the gym kicking ass. That's how it is done!

What is the problem with hair on men? In this day and age, men spend hours and large quantities of money trying to rid themselves of it. Chest waxing, eyebrow waxing, sack and crack waxing. No facial hair. No hair coming from nostrils or ears.

It beggars belief that they will go to any extreme to have a hairless body but spend a fucking fortune on hairstyling products and trips to the hairdresser (Note: I didn't say barbers. More on that later!)

I mean, what woman wants to go out with a man who spends more time in the bathroom than her and comes out looking more gorgeous as well!

Can you imagine film legend Charles Bronson, whose face was so craggy you could have climbed on it, smiling into the camera on an L'Oreal advert for men's face moisturiser saying, "Because I'm worth it."

I think fucking not.

I suspect Bronson washed his face in a solution of sea salt and vinegar. Anything less would have made him a wimp.

Back in my day, male grooming products were a 10p plastic comb and a bottle of Blue Stratos aftershave.

Occasionally, if you wanted that hair to stay in place if you were off to meet a female, you reluctantly stole a few sprays of Mum's Harmony hairspray and suspected you might be showing the first tendencies of being gay.

Can you now imagine the scene these days in the bedroom? Instead of the man lying in bed in anticipation of his lady coming out of the bathroom scantily clad and smelling like a desert rose, you now have the woman sat in bed impatiently tapping her fingers whilst her man shouts from the bathroom, "Can I borrow your overnight moisturiser, darling?"

Fucking wimp.

The only thing he should be wearing is protection and get on with the job at hand.

Back in the '70s, I could give a woman an orgasm just by looking at her.

Parading along a beach in a pair of Speedos and mirrored sunglasses females were fainting at our feet. That's a real man. Not some fairy looking for his Factor 30 lip balm to protect himself against the sun's deadly rays.

By the way, what's so wrong with chest hair? It didn't do Burt Reynolds, Tom Selleck, Sir Tom Jones or Chuck Norris any harm. If it is good enough for these legends, it should be good enough for you.

Not only were these men super cool, they were also legendary with the ladies and had legions of female fans.

Reynolds posed nude in the centre of Playboy magazine and that month they needed extra large staples.

Sir Tom Jones had so many pairs of ladies' panties thrown at him on stage he could have started up his own lingerie shop.

A woman should enjoy running her hands through some chest hair. It's got to be better than some bald chest. That would be like stroking some species of albino rat. Not exactly fucking exciting.

Men like Tom Selleck had so much chest hair; a female stroking it would probably find a team of pygmies playing a game of football in it. Plus, how could women resist his line of beach shorts. No filler in there!

Chuck Norris at one time must have been the hairiest killing machine on the planet, with the exception of King Kong. (Watch him in 'Way of the Dragon' fighting the incredible Bruce Lee.) He was everyone's hero, a Captain America that we all looked up to. What a role model for young guys. A true living all American hero.

Men like Reynolds, Selleck and Jones were sex gods and I believe chest hair had a lot to do with it. Plus, I also have it on good authority they were also hung like fucking donkeys!

To my horror, I have recently read about Veet hair remover for men. What in God's name is happening here? Hair is what defines a man. Why would you want to get rid of it? Yes, you may want to tidy up a few things, but actively using products to remove chest or genital hair is plain crazy.

As a young developing lad at school, you measured your journey into manhood by seeing if you were growing a fluffy moustache or beard, or whether you had begun to sprout a few chest hairs, or whether hair was forming on your balls.

The showers after sports period were when you furtively checked each other out to see the competition. Those sporting hair anywhere other than their heads immediately went up the pecking order in manliness. It was a badge of masculinity that we wore with pride.

Why when you reach manhood, would you work hard to rid yourself of it again? Alright, no man wants to take a women to bed looking like an extra from the *Planet of the Apes*, but in the same token, why would a man think a woman would want to take you to bed with your smooth chin, chest and bald bollocks? It would be like taking a ten year old schoolboy under the duvet with you, or a member of the boy band One Direction. It's not right!

If you are a bodybuilder, Chippendale, or male model, job and duty might dictate the need to remove man hair, but if you're not in those professions leave the hair alone and find something else to do.

Girls, do you want a lumberjack or a ballerina for a boyfriend? A Sean Bean or an Orlando Boom? A Gerard Butler or a Johnny Depp? Do you crave a man who wants to be drinking in your beauty when he is making love to you rather than one watching himself perform in the wardrobe mirror, checking if his hair is still in place?

What about a pure sexual man beast that doesn't mind working up a sweat and letting you strike a match on his chin stubble or crack the top off her bottle of pear cider on his washboard abs? Or do you want some lily livered girl boy who is frightened of the dark, thinks he suffers from PMT and prefers to order a skinny latte in Starbucks instead of a Doubleshot Americano?

Jack Daniels or a Bacardi and Coke? A steak and kidney pie or a cream slice? A great British fry-up or a croissant and jam? You get the picture.

Whilst we are on the subject of coffee, what is the deal with so many of them? Back in the day, if you went into a cafe, you either ordered a cup of tea or coffee. That was it. If again you were bordering on being 'camp,' you might go for a hot chocolate.

Now, when you enter Costa, Starbucks, Coffee 1 etc., you are confronted by a wallboard with an A-to-Z of drinks. You are scanning that board frantically for something you vaguely recognise when you are suddenly asked by a young Eastern Bloc girl behind the counter asking what you would like. And then panic sets in...

Suddenly, that board shrinks before your eyes. You see terrifying and strange names. Mocha, Frappucino, Double Latte, Espresso, Cappuccino! Where the hell is a normal coffee?!

When you finally settle on one, you are asked a dozen questions about it. It's like being on *Who Wants to Be a Millionaire*. "Do you want it with milk? Hot milk or cold milk? Skimmed milk or whole milk? Single shot or double shot? Small?

Standard? Large? Or is it Grande?" Do you want to phone a friend or run out down the fucking street crying?

Fucking hell. It's enough to make you give up drinking coffee for life. But it's worse with tea...

"A cup of tea, please."

"Yes sir. Do you want black, green, strawberry, lime, blackcurrant, Earl Grey, Darjeeling...?"

"Ahhhhh... Go away!"

Hot chocolate with cream and sprinkled chocolate flakes and marshmallows? No. Fuck off. What sort of man drinks that!

Also, when you are in a hurry and just want a takeaway coffee, there is always some pair of dithering bastards in front of you concocting the most complex drink on the planet where you would need a degree in biophysics and linguistics to understand it.

Coffee should be simple but it isn't. No wonder Columbia decided to export it to us and concentrate on drugs. A hell of a lot simpler I think. Can you imagine if it wasn't? Do you want your kilo of pure cocaine to have in or take out? Do you want a razor blade or credit card to cut it with sir?

Anyway, I digress...

But be prepared for that from time to time as we go along.

Right, now back to the business of manning up.

Men, we have spoken about ditching the pink. Now, kick the manbag into touch.

The only person that can get away with sporting one is Jack Bauer of *24*, a.k.a. Kiefer Sutherland. This is for two reasons:

- Firstly, in his bag, he carries manly items like big fucking guns, transmitters and explosives, plus his trusty, "I can get a signal anywhere" cell phone. Not an apple, banana, hair wax or a packet of mints. Okay?

- Secondly, he is a hard bastard. Who would dare take the piss and tell Jack Bauer he looked like a girl? Why take the risk of being disembowelled with a Gerber Mark II combat knife or having your head blown off from your shoulders by a fucking heavy duty Glock semi-automatic pistol?

You are not or never will be as cool or as fucking deadly as Jack Bauer. So get rid of it now. Enough said.

Next, do not let your girlfriend, wife or partner style you in any shape or form.

Be a man and decide yourself how you want to look. Let's face it, you are never going to style them, so why let them style you?

Look at some of the most popular celebrity males in the public eye. They have all been severely influenced by their fashion-conscious wives or girlfriends to the point of ridiculousness. Today, they have been transformed into male Barbie dolls. Now, I admire anybody for losing some weight, but to have your face suddenly look like a waxwork is unnatural. Why be botoxed and walk around with a look on your face that says you are totally surprised all the time. Again, any facial hair and, I suspect, body hair has gone completely. The sun bed manufacturers must be in love with these guys! Guys like this used to be a man's man. Now they're like a pet poodle. Men don't let this happen.

Sure, you don't want to walk around like some smelly, hairy knuckle dragger but there are limits to seriously crossing the gender barrier. Know what I'm saying?

What really pisses me off is when I am in a man's clotheswear section of a big store but I have to navigate my way around groups of women buying clothes for their husbands. What the fuck is all that about?

They are always in the way and when you try to pass them or want to look at an item of clothing on the same rail, they look at you as if to say, "What the hell are you doing here?"

Christ, there are precious little blokes' clothes shops as there are in comparison to women's. You females, keep the hell out of them, and men, what are you doing letting them pick your clothes! That is why most men of forty-to-fifty years old are dressed like seventy-to-eighty year olds.

I was in Asda the other day and saw some middle-aged woman picking out underwear for her bloke. How the fuck can a real man let his wife choose his pants? The only thing women should be worried about when it comes to a man's pants is what he has got in them! The other way around, yes, I think we males could have some input into a female's knickers, but that's a different story! If you do let a women buy your undercrackers, you will end up with a pack of bog standard briefs or boxers with the fucking day of the week printed on them or some stupid slogan like 'No Entry' or 'Made in Britain'. Very classy indeed when you drop your trousers.

Also, do not let the missus deck you out for holidays either. This is a big no-no. The open-toed sandals, baggy checked shorts and an XXXL t-shirt sporting 'I'm only here for the beer' doesn't cut it when you are off to foreign parts.

Have some self respect, guys. Choose and buy your own clothes. Otherwise, you will forever be decked out in a short sleeved nylon shirt, cream slacks and a cardigan.

Remember the rule. Real men choose their own clothes. Also remember... you don't wear pink!

Always have some imagination and style without looking a total asshole. Your wife is capable of making you look like one without your help.

Here is my plea to Burton... ban women now!

Now, before you females all get enraged, how would you like to see me rummaging around in your underwear and dresses on my own in Dorothy Perkins or Topshop?

On second thoughts the underwear...

Men age gracefully. Craggy features are landmarks of your time and experience on the planet. Forget Botox and face lifts. Why would you want to walk around with a look of total surprise on your face day and night? Be proud of that 'lived-in face' that shows character. That defines that you have 'been there'.

If you are in your fifties, do not dress like a twenty year old. You will look a prat. The hair gel, sunbed tan and earring won't hide the fact that you are middle-aged. Especially if your size thirty-eight gut is hanging over your thirty-two inch waist jeans like a flabby bum bag!

Be cool for your age but not an asshole. Think De Niro, Pacino, Samuel L Jackson, Willis, Brosnan, Nicholson, Springsteen, or Clooney.

Men that age well are like a fine wine, not old cheese. They are a fine wine; they're not trying to be a bottle of Smirnoff ice.

I noticed in recent years that a few of the 'old school' barbers shops are appearing once more. That is great news. In my youth, a barbers shop was a place for real men. No shampoo and blow dries there.

It was a place of scissors, razors, clippers, hot towels and a parting squirt of cologne.

It was always a male barber who merrily cut away at your hair while smoking a cigarette or slurping on a mug of manly black coffee.

The stereotypical gay hairdresser or the young blonde female with the fake tan and false boobs didn't exist.

It was a place of battered red leather sofas. The reading selection to browse while you waited mainly consisted of car or motorcycle magazine, or *Playboy, Penthouse* or good old *Knave* if you were lucky. A place also apart from Boots where you could purchase condoms, or as they were known then, a 'packet of three'. A total dream for a young growing and highly sexed lad.

Talk overheard was about the football, horseracing, the latest Clint Eastwood film or a Slade record. Or again, the subject of sex and females. It was the place to be for a teenage lad. A better learning environment, some may say, than school.

But shock horror...

Somewhere in the 80s, it all went badly downhill.

Whilst I agree there may be some perks to having your hair cut by a gorgeous twenty-one year old female named Shelley, Kirsty or Carly, it was all good until she opened her mouth and started asking questions like, "What shampoo and conditioner do you use?" or, "Are you going on holiday this year?"

As you struggled for an answer, she then unloaded her life history on you within ten minutes.

Suddenly you knew about her boyfriend Darren, her mum, sister, and her holiday to Ibiza and other useless information. How can any proper male sit in on all that shit? Four or five stylists I believe – yakking, bitching and uncontrollably laughing all together amongst the clipping of scissors. The constant drone of a hairdryer and some shit dance music megamix CD booming out. That is hell.

Thank God the barber is returning. So if you want to man up, get out of those poodle parlours! Stop talking about highlights, curling tongs and the possible bleaching of your eyelashes and get to a proper barber to discuss last night's footie, break wind and fantasise about shagging Cheryl Cole!

In modern times most married men turned into 'mincers'? Why do married men now prance about like a stereotypical feminine homosexual man than, well, most gay men? You married men out there need to fucking step it up a little and remember that you should be a Man, a Dad, a Leader, a Role Model. Just because you have a dick swinging between your legs doesn't make you a real man. A pair of bollocks might also be useful. Being a real man is something you earn, and that is to be respected and taken somewhat seriously.

People respect strength and when you are lacking that as a married man, it just makes you look that much more of a 'poof'.

When I was a kid, my old man didn't give a toss about designer labels or whether he had stocked up on hair gel. The only 'Boots' you would have found him in was working boots, he wasn't down the chemist shop rummaging through moisturisers! He didn't curl up on the sofa and watch *Jamie's Kitchen* or *The One Show* with a bar of 'Galaxy.' A Magnum to him was a big fuck off gun used by Clint Eastwood, not a girly ice cream. He watched sports, films and the news! He didn't give a crap about his diet and eating organic or gluten free. He wouldn't be seen dead tucking into a salad. It was meat and potatoes! A big bastard steak. Something that had to be killed, cooked and smashed onto a plate. As a young boy I identified being a man by using him as a role model.

A lot of men today are like cream puffs. As already stated, they use creams, oils and other girly things. If they aren't soft, then they're little baby-asses. They snivel about man flu and stress and 'throw their dummy out of the pram' if their wife or girlfriend doesn't treat them like mummy used too!

Men these days aren't the men of the Seventies. In fact, they act like kids, mainly little girls. They whine and complain constantly. They cry for their pseudo mummy/wife. .Couples that get married young seem to be the worst for this. These boys just weren't ready to leave Mummy's side just yet.

Some men see their wives as their mothers and revert back to being a ten year old. A spell in the fucking army or prison would soon sort them out.

Today is the era of the single parent; usually the women. Young boys take on feminine ways because they have no male role model to aspire to. Some women actually encourage the fact of turning their sons into being the daughter they never had even down to dressing them like a girl and encouraging a little make up and wearing mummy's jewellery Jesus Christ, it's enough to make the real men who have left this planet turn in their graves. This behaviour cannot bode well for the future of MANKIND. (Talking of Jesus note he had facial hair, He was a real a man.) What is it that turns a boy into a man these days? Back in my days at school you fought, you got the cane, a smack around the head or a blackboard rubber chucked at you, (oh shit sorry shouldn't of said black!) if you were out of line. You played football and rugby and got bested on cross country runs and P.E. sessions in the gym. Again if you were out of line in P.E. you got a size ten dap across your ass.

If you were ill, your Dad would check you out and unless your head was hanging off he would announce, "You're alright. Off to school." No excuses, no snivelling, just get on with it.

You were always looking for the next challenge to send you into manhood. Eventually you got bigger than your Dad and could outrun and outfight him and kick a ball harder.

The forces made a lot of boys men. Teaching them to stand on their own two feet, not looking for Mummy to cook their meals or wash their clothes. Or to iron their shirts and tuck them up in fucking bed with a hot chocolate. These men came out super-tough and super-efficient. They would stand up and fight for their families, and make their woman feel safe and secure.

Now the soft metro sexual couldn't fight sleep. They couldn't box an egg or batter a fish. He would struggle to open a car bonnet or a girl's bra. A mark of a man back in my day was when you could open a girl's bra with one hand or even better your teeth. Hell, bring it on baby! Men need more wardrobe space than a women and buy more glossy magazines than their girlfriend. They spend hours in Boots, Superdrug and Topshop and trekking around IKEA with one of those stupid yellow bags and a little wooden pencil.

Their gym workout is a fucking Zumba class or spinning. Confrontation and violence scare the shit out of them. They display all the symptoms of PMT.

Where will it all end? If they become a father, what will their son turn out like. I hate to fucking think.

When boys hit puberty and they get a bit of hair on their upper lip, their nipples swell for a while and their balls drop they need real men and real dads for male guidance and instruction. They need to be guided into manhood by a man, not a women or a wimp. Men are the providers, the protectors. Women are nurturers and home builders. If men aren't doing what you are naturally programmed to do, then you lose your identity.

Real boys out there, cut the apron strings, throw away the makeup and manbag and Abba CD's. Forget shaped eyebrows and fake tans. Step up to the plate. Stop letting females run your lives for you. Be a Man!

CHAPTER 2

Where Have All
the Real Men Gone?

Modern society has confused the male population. If we wander around like cavemen that is deemed as too extreme (I agree on this). But if we show our soft caring side, we are 'big softies'.

Knowing how to find the balance can be difficult for us. We are constantly teetering on the edge, in that realm of, "Did I get it right or not?"

Sometimes, you have got to grow a pair and do what you think is right, and live with the consequences.

I grew up being taught to be pleasant and polite to women. Open doors for them. Let them go first unless there is danger. Then you, the man, as the protector, go first. Never strike a woman or abuse her in any way. Be there for her when needed but don't be afraid to speak your mind and take control if required. Allowing somebody to have their way is not necessarily the RIGHT way!

I love being a knight in shining armour, riding to the help of a damsel in distress.

I have a certain code of ethics and I try to live by them. I do try to embrace change and modern society, but some of it I don't like or agree with, and I will stick to my old ways.

Back in my day, you would stick up for your girlfriend and fight for her cause. No questions asked. It was expected. It was one of those unwritten rules.

Today, though, a man can 'come a cropper' when the female he is defending says, "I could have handled that. I didn't need your help. Next time, keep out of it!"

On other occasions, after having taken a backseat presuming that was the right thing to do, a female will turn around and say, "Well, you weren't much help, were you? How could you just stand there and let them talk to me like that!"

Confused? You bet!

I am not saying I am one of those men against women's rights and all that stuff. I embrace that. I am not of the Gene Hunt, a.k.a. Phillip Glenister, of the brilliant TV show *Life on Mars* with his classic line, "As long as I have a hole in my ass, there will never be a woman Prime Minister!"

I like the 21st Century woman, but as I stated earlier, once the male lost his role as the hunter-gatherer, he sort of got fucked. He felt emasculated, and in some way, impotent.

Does a real man really want to be a house husband?

Wearing a pinny and rubber gloves. Feather duster in one hand and a fucking quiche in the other. I don't think so and deep down, is this what his wife wants to see in her man?

Does she want to come home to hear about his traumatic day with the washing or the big queue in Tesco? Or does she want her man hot and sweaty, coming in from a hard day's graft on a building site, shirt wide open to the navel, cracking a beer from the fridge, then taking her in his arms to give her a long passionate kiss and saying, "Give me half an hour to grab a shower. Forget the cooking. I'm taking you out for a meal."

Well?

Men have now been domesticated to within an inch of their lives. They are now attending yoga classes, counting contractions, bottling expressed breast milk and meeting their best mate in a coffee shop for a latte rather than down the pub for a swift pint.

Back in the day in any culture men were heroes. They were strong, wise and tough. The Brandos, Deans, Cagneys and Bogarts. Now, in film and music, a man is either a bully, a brute, a waster, a wife beater, a rapist, a thug, a clown, or a dithering clumsy fool.

No-one depicts a smart, decent man who loves his family but if he has to, will strap on a Uzi submachine gun to blast a gang of punks who have fucked with him.

TV, film, and media are powerful vehicles. How do you, as a male, want to be viewed?

When I was a boy, I was brought up on a diet of cowboy and war films. It was all great entertainment and innocent fun.

After watching these films, me and my mates would then go out and replay them in the local fields or school playgrounds. As far as I know, by shooting at each other with plastic guns we didn't grow up to go on some one-man slaughter with a real firearm through our local neighbourhood.

The cowboy films, no doubt looking back now, portrayed a jaundiced view of the Native American as the bad guy. But back then it either didn't occur to us or we didn't worry.

As a boy, you wanted to see shootouts, bows and arrows and wagon trains.

For me, the Western film was about shootouts, roping horses and drinking coffee around the camp fire, not anal sex (see: *Brokeback Mountain*).

I wonder what 'The Duke' Big John Wayne would have made of that kind of cowboy film!

Imagine Clint Eastwood playing the enigmatic bounty hunter – 'The Man with No Name' – suddenly going all gooey eyed over the local sheriff!

I used to watch war films with the same excitement. As a boy, you aren't going to be analysing the whys and wherefores of World War I, II, etc. You just wanted to see some tanks blowing up something and a lone solider singlehandedly charging a machinegun post with just a grenade and knife. Great stuff (although the Nineties did throw up some great war films, such as *Platoon, Hamburger Hill* and *Full Metal Jacket*). They wanted to bring home to the viewer the real horrors of war in some pretty gritty and non-patriotic action.

But back in the day, we just wanted 'boy's own stuff.' In my opinion, you can't beat films like *The Dirty Dozen*. What a line up of stars. Real tough guys led by the grizzly veteran Lee Marvin. He was a legend of pure granite male.

Or what about the fist pumping *Kelly's Heroes* or *Where Eagles Dare*? Where screen monsters like Richard Burton and Clint Eastwood were thrown together. Magic acting. Tough guys, tough action. Great entertainment. These guys were real men. Every lad my age wanted to be like them. Strong, fearless, noble heroes. (We will have more on real film heroes later).

Who does the young boy aspire to be like today? Who are the heroes, the tough guys, the role models? Where are the real men?

Now, most kids' heroes are some computer generated image in a Playstation game. Not a living, breathing person. What a shame.

Most of these 'characters' are bad guys with no ethics, no code or morals, no sense of right or wrong, good or bad.

They will steal, loot, stab, shoot and kill with no remorse or reason. Is this our modern day hero?

Deep down, every boy and man wants to be the real hero. The action man of the films. This still holds true, I believe, even today. Why do you think the James Bond franchise is still going strong?

I just fear that somewhere along the line, they will make Daniel Craig, the present Bond, become camp, start drinking cappuccinos instead of martinis and refuse to shoot that mad world dominating terrorist because it might violate his human rights. God forbid.

Real men want to be Bond. My favourite was Sean Connery. He had a hairy chest too, incidentally. Driving fast cars, swinging off bridges, shootouts, and jumping into bed with the world's most gorgeous women. Who wouldn't want that?

How could any man want to go to the cinema to watch the latest Hugh Grant or Ben Stiller offering in favour of Bond?

When I was a teenager, there were no such films as romantic comedies or 'chick flicks' (God, I hate that phrase). If you took a girl to the cinema, she watched the double bill that was showing. Simple as that. If it was *Death Wish* and *Rollerball*, so be it. Easy. The nearest thing to a romantic comedy was something like *Cannonball Run, Smokey and the Bandit,* or *Every Which Way But Loose.*

In the former, between crazy car chases, the love interest was Sally Field. In the latter, it was an orangutan named Clyde!

Another great example of the modern male having his real manly instincts being stifled was the amazing success of aforementioned BBC TV series *Life on Mars* which transported modern policeman Sam Tyler, played brilliantly by John Simm, back to '70s Britain to team up with DCI Gene Hunt, again played superbly by Phil Glenister.

Hunt was a throwback to the hard-man cop like John Thaw, a.k.a Jack Regan of *The Sweeney*. Foul mouthed, sexist, politically incorrect, hard drinking. Not adverse to a bribe or backhander but could still kick the shit out of some lowlife and lock them up and throw away the key.

Great TV viewing. Simply because most males secretly wanted to be Gene Hunt. Straightforward, uncomplicated and no bullshit.

No-one wanted to be Simm's Sam Tyler.

The success of the show was in the fact that today's modern man harboured admiration for Hunt and his methods. They couldn't believe that life, and in this case, policing, was like that in the Seventies.

Well, let me tell you. Although *Life on Mars* was a fictional show, every aspect of the '70s and Hunt was one hundred percent true. I lived it and knew guys like Hunt. They were real.

As a kid, a copper would clip you around the ear for fucking about and threaten to speak to your parents. As a drunken youth they would chuck you in the back of the police van and give you a few digs. It saved on all the paperwork and a court appearance. Fair enough.

Now guys, don't you wish you had lived in the liberated '70s? Of course you do.

A time where political correctness, health and safety and human rights red tape bullshit didn't exist.

How much more liberated our lives were before the overweening state started to muscle in on every aspect of human behaviour.

Instead of a female taking a trip to the industrial tribunal because of a sexist remark, she would respond instead with a sharp putdown or a slap around the face.

If a builder wolf-whistled from scaffolding at a pretty, young lady, instead of receiving a lawsuit, he got a cheeky flash of her knickers or the two finger salute. Either way, we laughed it off.

Men weren't afraid to be macho. Leather jackets, medallions and platform shoes were the order of the day.

Pubs were for smoking and getting drunk in. Cars for driving fast and their backseats for 'courting.'

Now this nanny culture, New Labour, puritanical Britain has stifled us. We are no longer allowed to enjoy ourselves. We live in fear of AIDS, UV ray skin cancer, liver disease, lung disease, MRSA and God knows what else. Everything is now bad or dangerous for us. What is safe anymore? Who knows?

What about all this, "I'm off work due to stress" bollocks? Look at these statistics below.

There is no doubt that working related stress is a serious problem for UK employers. In 2007-2008:

- 237,000 new cases of work related stress, depression or anxieties were reported in the previous 12 months.
- Nearly half a million people (442,000) in Britain reported work-related stress at a level that they believe is making them ill.
- Each case of stress-related ill-health leads to an average of 30 days off work.
- A total of thirteen and a half million working days are lost in Britain each year to work related stress.

As a young man starting work at fifteen, there was no such thing as stress. You just got your ass out and did a day's hard graft the same as my dad and his dad before.

What's all this lily-livered snivelling about how you can't handle the job and it's all too much for you. Man up, you big girl, and get on with it. Does your wife or girlfriend really want to hear you crying about your workload and deadlines and how your boss is such a bitch? Back in the day, you sucked it up and dug deep. You didn't have time off work unless you were going on holiday. If your work colleagues knew you were 'on the sick' due to stress they would have taken the piss out of you for the next six months. You never would've lived it down.

There are many times I felt the heat but I didn't take to my bed and fucking hide. No, you face it, sort it, and move on. If you can't stand the heat, get out of the kitchen. What do you want; your mummy, sorry wife, to write you a sick note or ring up your boss to tell them you're ill?

The same can be said for so called 'man flu'. Firstly, let's not even put the word man together with what is essentially a basic cold. No amount of pills, potions, and warm honey or hot water bottles will do anything for a common cold. It will run its course. Get over it, you big girl. Can you imagine great male world leaders, explorers, athletes and their like taking to their beds with the first sign of the sniffles? Think of men who dug coal from the mines, built bridges, dams, railways and skyscrapers, crying about a fucking runny nose and taking a week off work. Not likely. Man yourselves up and reclaim your manliness before you lose it for good.

Real men lead by example. Real men are hunters and leaders. They are solid, dependable and know their place. They are not frightened to show a female respect and love but also not frightened to speak up and take control from a woman when needed and live with the consequences.

It's no wonder men don't know their real place. This is the time to fight back. All you real men hiding out there, and you know who you are, time to stand up and be counted!

What's that you say? Only if the wife agrees... Shut it!

CHAPTER 3

The Misunderstood Male

Why is it that in this day and age, it is okay for females to be sexist and males cannot?

Let me give you an example. How many adverts on the TV depict a group of thirty-something women having coffee ogling the young gardener next door, stripped to the waist, mowing the lawn?

One of them will say something along the lines of, "He can sort my flowerbed out any time he likes."

They all have another look and laugh knowingly at each other. Swap the gardener for a waiter, surfer, construction worker etc. Well, you get the picture.

It's all clever, tongue-in-cheek humour. We all can relate to it. Harmless? Well, isn't it?

Now, let's re-run the advert. We have a group of thirty-something males sat outside a bar and they see a young lady across the road in a shop front window, dressing the mannequins.

One man says to another, "She can undress me any time she likes."

They all break into laughter, looking at each other with knowing winks. Harmless fun, eh?

But wait. No. There are outcries from certain female circles.

Sexist. Neanderthals. Male chauvinist pigs. Cavemen. Lechers. Dirty old men. Degrading. Disgusting., etc., etc.

You see, as I stated before, a man doesn't know where he's at and who he should be.

In adverts on the television today, most men are portrayed as bumbling, useless numbskulls.

Women are portrayed as smart, sassy, strong and confident.

Males are relegated to minor nuisances that have the odd use, but apart from that today's modern woman doesn't need him.

Now, I have no problem with equality. But this isn't. Men are now discriminated against. We have lost all our power. We have been neutered by the media because they think it's cool.

Bring back the surfer from the Old Spice adverts. That's what I say. A manly vision on our screens. Not some new age, baby-faced buffoon tripping over his own feet with his stupid, floppy hair falling in his eyes.

While we mention adverts, I am also sure that every male of my age will wholeheartedly agree when I say the adverts should bring back the Cadbury's Flake girl. Where is she? We males miss her terribly. Oh, sorry. Hang on. A sexist remark. That flake she is seductively eating is a phallic symbol for a man's dick! We can't have that. Disgusting.

Hey. But remember the Coca-Cola ads where a gang of women in an office ran to the window to watch the handsome, young window cleaner crack open a can of coke and seductively drink it, while they all leered and swooned at him? Hey. Wait. That's sexist isn't it? Was there an outcry from the male population? No.

You see what I'm getting at. Double standards.

Tell me now, I bet there wasn't a lady who didn't secretly want the Milk Tray man slipping into their bedroom at night to deliver his chocolates and a little extra.

But he's gone. Too macho. Too manly. He's got to be replaced with the geeky Mr Muscle guy cleaning the fucking bathroom.

Men are men. We are wired differently to females and we won't be changed.

I don't care if you have the most domesticated, loving man on the planet living with you, get him out with the boys and get enough beers in him and he will eventually be mooning out of a car window, openly pissing in a flower bed and flirting with the girl behind the bar.

We are still little boys who can find hours of amusement talking about breaking wind.

But for all that, a real man can, in the blink of an eye, turn into a trusty warrior and bodyguard to be by his woman's side.

Why, then, in this day and age, can't more males be depicted this way?

If this doesn't happen, men will not remember how the hell to act.

I can remember back in the '70s, *The Benny Hill Show* being slated by feminists as being sexist. This was a complete load of rubbish.

Yes, there was always a bevvy of scantily clad women on the show in his comedy sketches. But if you took time to watch it, the men always came out worst. The females were the victors. Whether they had to use their intelligence or their sexual charm, either way, the guy was a loser in the end.

Benny Hill was a comic genius but also openly gay. All the girls on the show loved him and said he was caring, considerate and a perfect gentleman.

So much for the leering pervert all those critics thought he was. I honestly can't see a problem with a man of any age looking at a pretty girl. It's human nature. If you didn't, I would presume his life is over.

Just because you grow old doesn't mean you have to lose all of your male instincts.

Men of a certain age can still pull something more than a muscle. Getting lucky doesn't have to mean finding a parking space in IKEA.

As the great American comic, George Burns, said, "I'm 90 and I still like to look at a pretty girl. Basically because looking is all I can do these days!"

My wife and I still enjoy a healthy sex live in our mid-fifties. We are into that Tantric sex like Sting advocates. We tried the plumber's position last Monday; we were both in all day but nobody fucking came!

Yesterday she said that she wanted to make love in the backseat of a car. Great, I thought. But no, she wanted me to drive! I digress again...

I have heard a female say when she dresses in a low-cut top or an ultra short skirt, "I do it because it make me feel good about myself."

Okay, that may be true, but you also have to know that you will have most red-blooded males taking a look at you. I don't think there's any woman naive enough to believe otherwise.

As a woman, would you rather feel attractive, wanted, even lusted after than being invisible, ignored and totally blanked by a man?

As a male, I would like to think a member of the opposite sex finds me attractive. Don't we all need an ego boost now and then?

My thoughts are, if you really don't want any unwanted male attention, then choose to wear something less revealing. It's simple.

Every male can't be labelled a pervert just because we glance at a female with fabulous breasts or a gorgeous pair of legs.

Don't women do this to men? Surely they do. Is that right or wrong?

Some have the view that the bigger a woman's breasts, the more stupid they are. I disagree. I find the bigger a woman's breasts, the more stupid I get! Women must have bigger breasts than other women otherwise how would a male boss know who to give the smaller pay check too?

Men are men. Women are women. Enjoy the fact.

In today's society, everybody seems to take themselves too seriously.

When interacting with the opposite sex, we think too much, read too much into their body language, what they say or do. We make relationships too complex and complicated.

I have been with the same women for 30 years now... for Christ's sake don't tell my wife!

Just look at the relationships of Rachel, Ross, Chandler, Monica, Joey and Phoebe in the classic US comedy show *Friends* How complex are they? Except one. Joey. He is the real male out of the three men.

If the shit was going to hit the fan, I'm sure every woman would go for him to protect her and every man to have him fighting by their side, rather than drippy Ross or girly Chandler.

Yes, I know, they are only acting but hopefully you get my point when it comes to males finding their own real identity instead of living a lie.

What amazes me sometimes is that everything that attracted a female to a male in the early days of their relationship, a woman tries to knock out of a man when they get married. Why? Don't these things still attract you now? Here is a joke for you while we are on this subject...

What food reduces a women's sex drive by ninety percent? Wedding cake!

Mrs Steele and I have been married 36 years and still fool around doing things we did the same as when we first met. You need to keep the flame burning. We didn't stop playing because we got old; we got old because we stopped playing.

As the late great Bob Monkhouse once lamented, "At my age I still like to sleep in the nude. It's not a problem... well only on long haul flights!"

Let's not be in any doubt guys, as manly as we strive to be, a female calls the shots when it comes to making love. It is on their say-so, no matter how you might convince yourself otherwise.

When you were going out together, you were at it like rabbits. Once the handcuffs of marriage click, it's like you suddenly joined a monastery. Out go the sexy undies and in come the cotton pyjamas and face pack. If she isn't in the mood or consents, then it isn't happening. Brutal but true.

Man has fought, cheated, begged, stolen, borrowed and killed for a chance to get his leg over. Sex has changed the face of history. Look at Henry VIII. He invented a whole new religion to have his evil way.

Males throughout history have pursued with relish and little thought or remorse the opposite sex in hope of taking them to bed. Women have a very strong bargaining tool when it comes down to it, and we men are utterly and totally obedient and docile when it comes to the promise of a shag.

We will mow the lawn, fix the guttering, mend the leaky tap and a whole host of other shit if we are on a promise. Never take anything for granted, lads, as that promise can be swiftly retracted at any moment, right up to the moment of entry! There is only so far you should go, men. Do not beg or plead for sex.

Fucking walk away at that stage and grab a beer and watch an episode of *Top Gear*.

Now here is the confusing issue. If a female tells you, "Not tonight, I'm not in the mood," a man has to take that on the chin and roll over or lock himself in the bathroom.

If a man says that to a woman, you will immediately come under interrogation. You will be asked, "Don't you fancy me?", "Are you ill?", "You're having an affair, aren't you? Seeing somebody else?" You just can't win. We have it hard when trying to work out a female.

In closing on this decidedly touchy subject, if there is any man out there now shaking his head and saying that this chapter isn't true and he doesn't look at other women or think about sex at weird moments, or hasn't thought about what it would be like to take your partner's best friend to bed, then they are lying. I had a thing for my next door neighbour for years but just couldn't bring myself to tell them my feelings. They moved last year... god how I miss Nigel! (Only joking men.)

I defy you to deny the following four things:

1. When you watched *X-Factor* back in the day, you thought about seeing Cheryl Cole naked on at least one occasion.

2. For you 'thinking' men of a certain age, when you watched *Countdown*, whilst racking your brains about the different numbers or letters being put up on the board, you glimpsed more than once at Carol Vorderman's or Rachel Riley's ass?

3. When two female tennis players are playing, you get turned on by their grunting and hope to steal a glimpse of their panties.

4. When you see a prim and proper female newsreader you wonder if she would.

Don't fucking deny it. Be a real man and own up to it now and then move on!

I recently saw a photograph of actress Christina Hendricks in the newspaper. Christina was promoting her latest TV series *Mad Men*.

It was a real pleasure to see such a gorgeous and voluptuous woman with real curves. Wow. What a change from having to view in newspapers, magazines and on TV, some size zero stick insect with all the sex appeal of a pubescent boy.

I love curvy women and it is a well documented fact that when a man stares at a full female figure the effect on his brain is comparable to that of beer or brandy. Amazing, eh?

I like a woman to be a woman. I don't want to see the wiry physique of a Madonna. It's almost masculine. I want to see the soft full curves of a Nigella Lawson. A cooking goddess.

I am not mildly interested in a flat chested waif like Keira Knightly. Give me a Marilyn Monroe figure any day.

Hendricks isn't afraid to flaunt her 36DD assets. She knows we are staring like little puppy dogs. So what? She is all women and leaves us males in no doubt.

Fashion has depicted painfully skinny models to wear their clothes, but if you are selling sex, use size 12+ girls with all the right lumps and bumps.

We want more women gracing our televisions and cinemas that are not afraid to show their curves. This is what every real red-blooded man craves.

Tell me why singer Rhianna is in the newspaper every day in some stage of undress? Who cares? It does absolutely nothing for me. Yet everyday without fail she is in them with some meaningless piece of trash written to accompany a photograph of her ass. Big deal.

Study this list of beauties, past and present, and smile in contentment that you are blessed to have looked at them:

Christina Hendricks, Nigella Lawson, Kate Winslet, Kelly Brook, Beyoncé, Kim Basinger, Jacqueline Bisset, Debbie Harry, Cheryl Ladd, Sharon Stone, Lynda Carter, Bo Derek. Raquel Welch, Sophia Loren, Marilyn Monroe, Jean Harlow, Holly Willoughby, Kim Kardashian, Jennifer Hudson, Rachel Weisz, Martine McCutcheon... The list could go on and on.

Praise be for real women. Clinton Steele knows what he is talking about.

Men are PCed to death. The consequences of almost fifty years of ardent feminism have been devastating: society. Men are in total confusion about gender roles, the rise of a class of ball-busting bitches whose battle cry is, "We don't need men," trumped-up charges of "date rape" and "sexual harassment," angry women blaming men for all their hang ups. In brief, an overall erosion of a male's confidence.

As society becomes more and more feminized, younger men that are being brought up by single mothers who don't have a clue about the male sex drive but who teach their sons to surrender their natural masculinity and pander to women, today's man is forced to bow down and apologize for his inherent male sexuality.

Pleasing women

This demise of sexual confidence has resulted in a world full of male wimps and doormats.

Today's male tiptoes around on eggshells, afraid of saying the "wrong thing", scared of showing his natural sexual interest in a woman, frightened of being ridiculed, humiliated, or even fired, scared of his own true self..He is worried he will be labelled a sexist pig or pervert.

For years now, men have been forced to bend over backwards to please women, by pandering to a self-serving social movement that should stop fucking with the hard wiring of five billion years of human evolution.

This observation is lost on the female population because women just don't have a fucking clue what it is to be truly sexual. A female's sex drive can't even begin to measure up to a male's. Yet modern feminism still stupidly works to feminize men into submission. Nature intended men to be strong, assertive, bold, and sexual. This is why testosterone powers through their bloodstreams not oestrogen. This is why they have balls not breasts. This is a man's God given gift; it is his heritage and pedigree as a member of the male gender.

And the truth is, despite what females say and how much they protest, they secretly a man who acts like a real man. Poke below the surface and you'll discover that women don't really want a man to act like a female any more than a guy wants a woman to be butch and masculine.

Just as an observation, when a woman acts like a man, why can't she act like a nice man instead of an asshole! Swearing, pissing in public and puking up all over yourself is the greatest turn on. Also a discreet tattoo on your left buttock or lower back is sexy and feminine, having a couple of full on sleeves of tattoos is like taking an a big hairy biker to bed.

It's high time to stop letting women take a big pair of shears to our nuts .It's time for men to stop apologizing for being a fucking man. It's time instead to totally celebrate their sexual nature, and to reclaim their sexual confidence. Now go and watch the *Dirty Dozen* or *A Fistful of Dollars* with a six pack to reclaim your manliness.

How do you become a sexually confident male?

To really transform yourself you must be mentally strong and re-programme the shit women have sold you. Let's look firstly at what you don't want to be or do.

- Seek approval from women.
- Cater or pander to women.
- Be predictable and boring.
- Be on your phone calling women every day or worse, many times a day (talking about trivial shit and reminding her constantly how wonderful she is).
- Buying her meals, gifts, washing up and hoover etc to buy favour.
- Don't be nervous, insecure or overly nice around women. Use a bit of the treat them mean keep them keen tactics.
- Remember you are not her girl friend .You are her man. Men provide solutions ,girlfriends provide sympathy
- Do not jump and be like a lap dog with one text from her phone. I have seen men taking a piss and answering the phone to their missus. Get real.
- To not stand for rude behaviour, cancelled dates, lateness, stupid mood swings or generally playing mind games. etc.
- Do not sell yourself out totally to please women in the hope of getting a fuck. E.g. Helping bake cupcakes in the kitchen and agreeing you like her latest *Take That* CD.
- Are afraid that if they do "something or say something wrong", she'll pack up and leave them. Then you have a shallow relationship in the first place, don't you?

- Never beg or grovel for sex like a fucking pathetic wimp. If it ain't happening take up a hobby or something or check out some porn on the computer. You will know it's getting desperate if you are getting turned on by females on the front of 'women's weekly and 'Knitting world's magazines'.
- Do not fuck yourself up and over-analyze everything women say and do.
- Natural sexual urges is nothing to be guilty about..
- Do not be manipulated by females and be used like 'an instant credit card'. Men that do this…
- Are fucking useless in bed.
- Are shit scared to speak their mind in case it offends.
- Can't complain about or correct a woman, nor mention that her cooking is shit, or her bum does look big in that dress and yes you do talk too much.

The total opposite of all these things will bring you sexual confidence. To get an idea about what sexual confidence is, just observe any self-labelled "bad boy" in action – they are arrogant, selfish fuckers, but they always have a beautiful women on their arm. Why is this? Why are women attracted to these guys? Because at the end of the day women are emotional and when that happens the higher thinking part of her brain disengages. They find these types of males sexually exciting. Also maybe, just maybe they might be the one to change him.

Sexual confidence is demonstrated in the following ways.

- You become a challenge, not a doormat. You will not make excuses for who they are – you will radiate sexuality and be comfortable with your natural masculinity.

- You will now become a catch for a woman, not the other way around. You will become unpredictable and untamed. You will not be stifled.
- You will not be afraid of being you. who they are.
- You will have no interest in being PC sacrificing your true identity to gain female approval, or being overly nice.
- You will not need to exchange money or presents for sex (a.k.a. "dating").
- You will control the relationship always.
- No female BS will be stood for.
- Your body language will radiate MAN.
- You can flirt with ease.
- You will become a natural leader, not a follower.
- You can unashamedly look at women's bodies without fear of reprise.
- You will not care if they score with a particular woman, because they know that there are many more pebbles on the beach.
- Never apologize for who they are. Act like a real man around women not a wimp.
- If a woman has a hormonal outburst don't be afraid to tell her to shut the fuck up.

In plain terms, sexually confident men aren't afraid to be themselves or to exert their natural sexuality and don't really care what society thinks of them. They are true men, just as nature intended.

Do not confuse real men with 'Bad Boys' Real sexually confident men are not abusive towards women – in fact, they love to be in the company of women and will look after them very well. Real women won't be able to keep their hands off them.

Being a man

To be a real man you don't have to have the looks of Clooney or the body of a Chippendale to be sexually confident and attract women. But you will have to dig into your natural manly resources and let it shine out for the female population to see.

When a man does this he can step into a room full of people and turn heads .He will have charisma and charm. He will attract females like a magnet and have the respect of fellow males.

Women can stare into his face and read his body language and instantly know that he's a sex god (note; Reynolds, Selleck, Clooney, Butler). Instead of wantonly seeking the approval of women and tripping after them like a little puppy dog, he is now the "one desired," and women pursue him because he has transformed himself from a fucking doormat into a prize that needs to be fought for.(note; James Bond).

Don't live your life pretending to be something else. You must be true to your heritage and all the real men who have gone down in history.

Do not suppress your masculinity because you have been told it's not cool or outdated. When the shit hits the fan, a woman will want a real man to spring into action and take control, not be cowering and whimpering behind her skirts and looking to phone mummy.

Men like to look at women. They love real women who are not afraid to be a size fourteen. Not afraid to flirt and be sexy Real men are not shy to tell their lover what turns them on and do it. No hiding under the bedcovers with the light off when it comes to love making. If you like it and it doesn't hurt or offend anyone, then get on with it with the light on or the curtains open.

Real women like their man to be assertive in the bedroom and not afraid to work up a sweat and be dirty. Be in control, imaginative and never boring.

Real women are not the stereotyped blonde bimbo or catwalk model; those are fantasy images and females that adapt to these images are plastic and false. *The only way is not fucking Essex.* It takes many hours of makeover hell by professionals to get females to look like this. They will not look like this the morning after, men. There will be more left at the bedside than in the bed. A lot of plastic fantasy women are actually boring in bed. Why use live ammo on a dead target.

Real women can be found at every supermarket, coffee shop, school playground or petrol station. They are everywhere if you look, exuding sexuality and beauty.(check out Bruce 'The Boss' Springsteen's record *I'm in Love with the Queen of the Supermarket.*)

A real woman is hiding in many a female just waiting to come out. Lots of guys are spending their time chasing after some feather brained temp when they have a real women at home but don't see it.

Real women have a real life, not one out of a fucking glossy magazine. They have more to deal with in their world than a chipped nail, an appointment with a sunbed or a bad hair day.

They have tough jobs; deal with bringing up children and sorting domestic chores. But when they have time to glam up and chill out, they are tigresses in the bedroom. Sometimes, guys, we are looking in all the wrong places for a real women.

A few of the many things that turn Clinton Steele on about a real woman:

- A woman's scent
- Wet 'step out of the shower' hair
- Sexy, classy underwear
- Her legs
- Talking dirty in bed
- Taking the lead in bed
- Little things that make her *her*
- Complimenting you unexpectantly
- Showing affection in public
- Being risky and sexy with you in public
- Painted finger and toe nails
- Stockings
- A lovely shaped bum in a tight dress, jeans or leggings
- A coy smile
- A hair flick
- A fluttering eye lash
- A stiletto shoe dangling from a foot
- A flash of cleavage or thigh
- Watching a her dress or undress
- Watching her put on her makeup and brush her hair
- Smile
- Soft touch
- Vulnerability, but also strength

The list goes on...

Clinton Steele's list of things that will fail you in bed with a female:

- Not kissing first. .Jumping straight in downstairs isn't the way to go. Tease your way up to things steadily. A passionate kiss is the starter for ten.
- Squeezing her breasts. Don't do it in the manner that you are testing for the ripeness of a melon. Gently stroke and touch. They are not putty.
- Biting or playing with her nipples. Remember you are not tuning Radio One in or chewing a caramel. Do not clamp down on them like Rottweiler on heat. They are highly sensitive. Teasing, licking, gently sucking is the preferred method. Stroking her gently through her panties is erotic and sexy. Yanking her knickers up her crotch can piss her off as well as not lovingly giving quality time to her other body parts. Again, don't just hone in on the big guns. Pay attention to her hair, neck, ears, nose, inner arms, thighs, fingers and toes. Stroke, kiss and lick slowly. Take your time before you hunt down the good stuff. A female likes to be teased up the ladder of pleasure.
- Don't take a time out. Once you start, you must slowly and steadily keep going. Don't let her go off the boil. It is harder for a female to get back in the mood. Think of a steady jog not a sprint.
- Going too fast. When you get down to intercourse, don't go at it like you are drilling for oil. Your willy isn't a DVD recorder either. Remember no pause, fast forward and eject. Going too hard. Easy does it. You don't have to break the bed or her pelvis. Don't ask her if she has had an orgasm. As a good lover you will know. Please also don't ask did you fake that?

Don't come too soon – find as many ways as possible to pleasure her before the moment of release. As a man matures he can keep a rein on things a lot longer than his young counterparts. But also don't fuck around forever otherwise she won't be able to walk the next day and your dick will look like you put it on a barbecue. Also don't wipe your dick on the duvet after, get some tissues please. **If she is heading south on you, be a gentleman and let her know if you are about to 'blow'!**

CHAPTER 4

The Nanny Nation

Written by Kevin O'Hagan

I read recently in a newspaper that a school banned children from playing marbles in their break time as it was deemed too dangerous. Can you believe that? Am I losing my marbles or have the soft bellied Health and Safety brigade gone totally mad?

But wait; there is more health and safety madness.

Here is a brief selection:

• Hanging flow baskets from lamp posts have to be checked by an engineer at £70 a time to make sure they will not fall down.

• Serving tea was banned at a garden fête. It was deemed too dangerous in case somebody burned themselves on the tea urns.

• Ironing boards were removed from a caravan site after officials said users could burn themselves.

• A historical re-enactment that wanted to chop vegetables as part of their act were told they would have to be tested on their slicing and dicing skills to perform in public.

• Officials are trying to ban ice cream van chimes as they disturb the peace and offend certain people. What the fuck? How long does a chime go on for? It is to briefly let a neighbourhood know a van is on their street. So unless somebody is sat at their front window all day, how the hell will you know a van is there! What next? Banning ambulance and fire engine sirens because they are too noisy?

Meanwhile, back at school, a class was banned from hanging their pictures up on windows with Blu-Tack in case it reacted with a chemical in the glass and exploded. Yes, I kid you not. Even when the manufacturers of the product said it was perfectly safe to use on glass, the pictures came down. Complete and utter madness.

We've already had conkers banned in school and no doubt, Hopscotch, Kiss Chase and Off-Ground Touch because of life threatening consequences of playing them.

Tell me, what does a kid do now in their lunch breaks?

If this madness pursues, they will be frightened to sneeze too hard in case they drive their nasal bones unexpectedly up into their brain and die!

I went to school in the '70s where we played all manner of games that carried an element of risk. But hey, wasn't that what made them exciting? Of course it was.

Here is a 'by no means exhaustive' list for those of my age to reminisce about:

- British Bulldog (Oh my God – am I allowed to say British?)
- Murder Ball
- Crab Football
- Touch Rugby
- Slaps
- Knuckles
- Piggyback Fights
- Pile Ons
- Splits

If you don't know anything about these games, get on the internet and Google them before they are forgotten for good.

I participated in all the above and lived to tell the tale, and I went on to have a pretty normal and healthy adulthood.

I fear in this day and age if things carry on the way they are, the future young generation will be wrapped up in cotton wool and never be allowed to fulfil their potential.

Where, then, will all our great leaders – warriors, explorers, sportsmen – come from?

Throughout history, we have had great adventurous people climb the highest mountains, navigate unchartered seas and cross deserts and icy wastelands. Will we see that again?

These people and millions more, embraced their fears, faced them and became better people because of it. Their names have gone down in the history books.

These days, most children spend time in the safety of their bedrooms playing on their DS, Xbox, Playstation, Wii, etc. They are living their adventures and feeling fear and the adrenaline rush through a virtual experience. But it's not real.

Okay, some can argue that children are no longer safe to go out to the local park or playground because of paedophiles and muggers.

So, as a parent, find time to go with them!

My dad taught me to play football, climb trees, fish, play pitch-and-putt golf, swim in the sea, wrestle, box, and loads of other things. A group of my mates and I would trek off to the local fields and woods building tree houses, searching for birds' eggs, swimming in streams and swinging off of a rope over a lake, from and other fun things.

Yes, some of the things I faced because they did carry a risk. But mostly, they were things outside of my comfort zone. But the more you experienced them, the easier it got.

I think that all children should experience acceptable risk. I don't mean doing something stupid like running across railway tracks or diving off a crane overlooking the local docks — things that have been done!

But if schools start mollycoddling them at a young age, they will fear everything.

In most schools, you can't promote the concept of winning or losing.

Take, for example, the school sports day. Everyone has got to be a winner. It is not right for a child to be classed as a loser. What a load of bollocks.

How can we get people to develop a winning mentality if it is suppressed?

God knows, Great Britain is not blessed with hoards of winning sports stars. We have regularly been second best or worse for many years.

Does this go back to the above observation?

In my school days, there were exceptional sporting individuals and you knew you couldn't compete equally against them, but they were still liked and nobody took offence that they could beat you in a running or swimming race.

Anyway, if you wanted to compete with them and give them a run for their money, you would have to get off your lazy ass and put the work in, rather than be soft-soaped that everything was okay and you were a winner for having a go.

Yes, it's nice to get a bronze medal, even better to get a silver, but everyone who competes wants the gold, don't they?

You don't agree? Then I'm afraid you're not a true winner.

What's wrong with wanting to be first, to be successful and to be a winner?

As long as you don't hurt anybody in the process, then it should be encouraged. Otherwise, where will our next Olympic champion come from, or successful international football team, etc...?

When I first took up martial arts as a fourteen year old boy, you bet I was scared. I joined my first class on my own. It was filled with full-grown men punching, kicking and striking each other. I was by far the youngest there. I was certainly intimidated, but I wanted to do it so badly the need to learn overrode my fear.

After a few months I was accepted, and began to feel more comfortable in the hard training environment. I earned the older guys respect and even senior grades acknowledged me.

Whenever, though, it came around to sparring, you would still get that rush of adrenaline and if you mistook it for fear, you wouldn't show up to train or find some excuse not to get on the mats.

It is human nature to find an excuse at every turn. It's a lot harder to step into the arena and try.

I have been a practicing martial artist for more years than I care to remember. Throughout that time, I have met many challenges and put myself to the test on more occasions than I can count.

I grew by facing my fears, and through the path of martial arts, I also learnt to face other obstacles and barriers that cropped up in life.

I have taught martial arts to children from the ages of 5 to 16.

As long as you teach professionally, you can expose them to contact training, sparring, grappling without fear. It builds their bodies and their minds. It gives them confidence, a sense of purpose and belonging. It teaches them to step up and face their fears.

I see lots of different personalities. Kids that are confident, cocky, full of themselves. Others are shy, reserved, and timid. But all benefit and blossom.

They certainly learn about winning and losing. Success and failure. Because that is life. If you can learn to live with your winning moments and your losing ones, then you will survive life.

I teach this and will not bow to parental peer pressure when they feel their child is ready to grade for their next belt. That is my decision and through experience, I will know if, and when, they are ready.

I have had children cry when they didn't pass a grade or lost a fight. Others get annoyed. Some moan to their parents. Others will glare at me as if I was the Antichrist himself reincarnated. But they learn. Life can be tough. It is not always a bowl of cherries. One must learn to deal with disappointment but be determined to come back twice as strong next time in order to succeed.

The culture of today, for many, is they want it now. They can't wait and won't wait.

They don't want to put in the time or effort. They want the quick route, the fast track, the shortcut to success.

As the famous American inspirational speaker Zig Ziglar once said, "Ladies and gentlemen, the lift to success is out of order, but you can always take the stairs."

When children in my class get frustrated because they can't pick up a technique I have shown, I will say, "How many times have you practiced it?"

"A dozen or more", might be the reply.

"Well, drill it another dozen, then another and see how it feels."

I always use a famous sportsperson as an example to illustrate the point.

I would say, "How often do you think David Beckham worked on scoring from his free kicks or Johnny Wilkinson on his kicking? Certainly not a few dozen times."

To become the best, they do it thousands of times. Even when their teammates have left the practice field, they would be there practicing their kicks. That's how you become good at something.

There is no quick way unless you are blessed with exceptional skills. Even then, they have to be improved and bettered.

As you step up into a bigger and better arena, then your skills have to improve, too.

For me, that's why I was on the mats training for a big percentage of my 50+ years. To be the best I could and aspire to my peers.

That's what has kept me going through thousands of throws, rounds on the bags and pads, hours of grappling on the ground, sparring opponent after opponent, and working through belt grades over and over.

I always felt I could be better and still do in no matter what pursuit I follow.

I have had great success but also some bitter disappointments. But I have always had the mental strength to pick myself up and go again. What's the alternative? Giving in or giving up is not an option.

This attitude of mine was developed from a young age.

My dad would not let me hide from my fears but would help me face them. Yes, it was scary but I knew it was the right thing to do in the long run.

I have developed this in my own children who are now grown up and are their own person. I know they have not only the physical skills to survive, through their martial arts training, but also the mental strength to take on life's ups-and-downs.

When I was at junior school, I hated swimming and I remember my swimming instructor as a tough and unsympathetic woman who would come out with spoken pearls of wisdom such as, "Don't worry if you swallow the water in the pool... there's plenty more!"

I hated her, but in the end she got me out of the shallow end and into the deep end and swimming. It took time and much haranguing from her, but she did it.

I can honestly say that every Wednesday when the swimming class came around I was concocting a dozen reasons not to go to it, and my mum, love her, was so soft that she would have written me a sick note every time. But something in me told me to go and face up to it.

I am glad I did, and I owe Mrs Grumpy Swimming Instructor a debt of thanks. Later in life, I signed up to enter the Swimathon for charity and swam a hundred lengths of an Olympic sized pool. I wouldn't have experienced that if I had given up at the first hurdle.

It doesn't matter how fast you are moving as long as you are travelling in the right direction.

Every individual will have a different learning speed but that is not as important as finally reaching your goal.

It doesn't matter if it takes six months or six years.

If you want to climb Everest, you are not just going to go out there and do it straight away. You will train on many smaller climbs first, gaining experience and knowledge, until finally you are ready for the big one.

I train a fight team who compete in MMA/cage fighting. If I have an individual come to me and tell me he wants to be a professional cage fighter, then he will start a long and arduous journey. He will not just step in there. Gradually, he will build the necessary skills, fitness and craft to be able to step into this arena and be a hundred percent physically and mentally ready.

It's the same with anything you want to achieve. As the old saying goes, "There is no such thing as a free lunch."

I was watching a programme recently which starred celebrity Justin Lee Collins. Each week, he would take up a challenge and go through the training necessary to achieve it.

The episode which stuck in my mind was when he trained to be a high diver.

He started his training in Soundwell Swimming Baths, a local and well-known bath in my hometown of Bristol. In fact, it was one of the baths where I experienced my nightmare swimming lessons when I was a boy.

There is a high diving platform there which, as a kid, I always watched in awe as certain individuals would seemingly fearlessly climb the ladder and dive off.

I never got to a stage where I could bring myself to do it.

Justin told the same sort of story. He had no diving experience at all.

He started diving from the pool's edge over and over and over with his coach. Then, he moved on to diving from a raised block. Then next, onto a small springboard.

He was then taken up country to another pool where there were multiple diving platforms of all sizes.

His coach took him to the very top one, which was, I believe around sixty feet and they just sat on the edge and looked down. Even this frightened the living daylights out of Justin, and he had to go back down.

His coach told him that he would have him diving off that eventually, and Justin gave him a look of shocked horror and disbelief.

He carried on his training each day, slowly diving from ten feet, then twenty feet and so on, until the day came when he walked up to the end of that sixty feet platform and performed a perfect dive, not just once but half a dozen times.

It was absolutely amazing what he achieved. He overcame so many fears, plus a perforated eardrum, to achieve his goal.

It was an inspiring piece of TV and just another example of what can be achieved through perseverance and belief.

I love reading or watching inspirational stuff. Individuals that broke the mould and stepped up to the plate and achieved greatness.

Throughout history, the world has produced many greats, from great explorers such as Captain Cook, Raleigh, Livingstone, and Captain Scott, to great warriors like Richard the Lionheart, Lord Nelson, William Wallace, Lawrence of Arabia, through modern-day greats in their field – Ranulph Fiennes, Muhammad Ali, Sir Steve Redgrave, Pelé, Roger Federer, Michael Jordan... the list is endless.

We all have our favourites. I will bet that from young children, each and every one of these individuals had something in them to make them want to be different and achieve. To leave their mark in the history books.

They weren't going to do this through being banned from playing marbles or conkers.

We, as human beings, are built for action, built to do, built to achieve; not sit and vegetate.

We only get one shot on this planet. We need to think of our lives as a big, blank book which is given to us at birth. Now, it is up to us to fill those pages with life. Each page should contain something new, exciting and different.

We achieve enlightenment through adversity, not sat on our asses waiting for our lives to take off. You, as an individual, have got to make it happen or at least die trying.

Success is a journey, not a destination. We have to experience discomfort in order to grow. That is a fact.

Maybe I come from an era that views things differently. I did come from a time where a teacher gave you the cane, or chucked a blackboard rubber at your head, and it was the norm, not cause for a teacher to be suspended and splashed all over the Sunday papers.

No matter if you agree or not, as a kid you knew the line you could push to and what you were going to get if you went beyond.

I had a few occasions with the cane, blackboard rubber, slap around the head, and plimsoll across the ass, etc. It hasn't traumatised me or turned me into a serial killer.

I probably deserved it for doing something I shouldn't have been doing but did it anyway. We are back to acceptable risk.

If, for example, you thought the risk of having a smoke behind the bike shed was worth two or three strikes of the cane, so be it!

There is no point crying 'child abuse' once you were caught at it and caned. Suck it up and get on with it.

For me, today's society is too soft. As soon as corporal punishment went out of the schools so did any fear, respect or line in the sand.

Yes, some teachers in the minority abused it. But most had some sort of deterrent.

Now, they are impotent and powerless. Their hands tied with red tape, human rights and protocol.

Am I an outdated dinosaur? In some people's eyes, no doubt I am. But we can all have our opinions and mine is fucking right!

Kids in this day and age need focus. They need a goal. Something to take them off the streets.

When I was a kid I would play in my back garden for hours. Especially during the school holidays. I had a good friend that used to come down and stay with his Nan, who happened to be one of my neighbours.

We played all sorts of shit made up from our young imaginations: Cowboys and Indians (oh sorry, Native Americans), War, James Bond, Bruce Lee, wrestling, cricket, football and many more.

We used to fashion a whole host of lethal weaponry out of bits and pieces of wood my old man had lying around the garden.

Out would come the hammer, nails and saw, and in no time at all a sword, axe, or dagger would be crudely made, and we'd re-enact *Arthur of the Britons*. Remember that programme starring Olivier Tobias as the cool and ultra-tough Arthur? He was a sword-wielding genius. His party piece was to drop his sword on the ground but cleverly flip it back up into his hands with a flick of his foot and then effortlessly dispatch his would-be assailants. We would try for hours to perfect this skill.

Along with him were his sidekicks, the blond haired axe carrying Kai, and the old grizzly one-handed warrior Lud. These were classic TV heroes. Enough to get any young lad's blood pumping and testosterone flowing.

Back then, play was rough and tough. No room for cry-babies. We would joyfully attempt to whack ten bells out of each other with an array of self made weapons. We skinned knuckles, bruised shins and had lumps and bumps on our heads. But we were fine and always shared a glass of orange squash and a chocolate biscuit after battle, still the best of buddies.

We also had a vast collection of toy guns, ranging from Colt .45 pistols, to semi-automatic handguns, to rifles and submachine guns, depending on what we were playing.

When we got into Bruce Lee and Kung Fu, our weapon making skills went into overdrive. We knocked out a whole host of exotic weapons that we had no real idea what they were. We had just seen them in magazines or on the TV. We would swing them around like lunatics until they eventually came apart, and a good portion of them would end up flying into a neighbour's garden.

This was real boy's own stuff. Working up a sweat, covered in grass stains and mud. Magic days. A thousand times better than being sat brain dead in front of a computer screen. Plus, it kept us fit and skinny as rakes. No child obesity problems here. There was more fat on a chip than us.

The sun would seemingly shine endlessly back then. Very rarely did rain stop play. If it did, it was time to make a tent out of your mum's old clothes horse and a blanket, or retire into the house to play with the Action Men or Matchbox cars.

I loved those Action Men. You were someone back then if you owned one. For me, the original one was best, but the one with real hair and the later one that spoke were welcome additions. Every boy wanted one just as every girl wanted a Barbie or Cindy doll.

Where are the Action Men now? They have faded into obscurity. It is no longer politically correct to play war games. Action Man is out of favour. Deemed too violent, yet you can blast ten shades of shit out of someone on computer games such as *Call of Duty* and their like!

We can't encourage young boys playing with Action Men and glorifying war. How dare they emulate their heroes? We mustn't encourage this, yet the media are crying out to help our heroes in the real war zones around the globe. Maybe a young lad playing with an Action Man could do his bit in recognising our real heroes out there in the forces!

The toys back in the Seventies were made to last, not like the cheap plastic shit of today. You play with it on Christmas Day and it is broken by Boxing Day.

Back in the day, cars were made from die cast metal. They were sturdy and durable. Smash them into a wall or drive them off a flight of stairs and there wouldn't be a scratch on them. Remember the mighty Tonka toys. The diggers and cranes, etc. were virtually indestructible.

What about the Batmobile? The James Bond car? The Captain Scarlet car? Then the Thunderbirds vehicles? All absolutely brilliant. They had opening doors, flying projectiles and missiles, ejector seats, flashing lights and sirens. These toys were built to last and entertain. The same can be said for Corgi and Matchbox cars. Now these things are all collectors' items that fetch a good price.

Everything now is rehashed and a much poorer quality. They have no heart or soul. No loving care has been put into their manufacture.

The action figures of today are poor and overpriced imitations of the early Marvel figures, Thundercats, He-Man, Ghostbusters, Spawn, or Alien series. These figures were hard wearing and genuinely real.

Modern day shops such as the Forbidden Planet, thank God, try to keep the genre and standards.

It is a sad testament to today's child that most big chain toy shops are closed or closing. Giants such as the American chain Fao Swartz are all gone, the UK's Beatties and their like are bankrupted and obsolete. Even Toys R Us is struggling. The big percentage of their stores are now computer games. Sad news.

I believe our country's soldiers, explorers, sportsmen and adventurers all got their inspiration and ambition from playing with simple toys and boys own games played out in back gardens, parks and fields. Add a healthy dose of Marvel and DC comics along with the Victor, Hotspur, and Eagle and our future heroes were born. Boys knew they were boys.

I am afraid Mario and Donkey Kong aren't going to produce any world beaters in the future. The safety of the sofa isn't where heroes are born. We need new trail blazers. In my day, this started when you first had the imagination to pick up a toy and play.

Maybe Action Men will one day reappear, but I fear he will be sporting a Burberry cap, Ben Sherman shirt and a pair of tracksuit bottoms!

Where have all the youth clubs gone? When I was a teenager growing up, there were loads of them.

They were a meeting place for us. You had a sense of belonging and camaraderie there. It gave you a purpose, got you off the streets and away from getting up to no good.

The youth clubs I went to belonged to the church and normally, a priest would organise it and have some participation in its running along with the youth leaders.

You had all sorts of activities there and both sexes mixed merrily together playing football, rounders, cricket, netball and table tennis.

Music was played. There had a tuck shop of crisps, chocolate, sweets and soft drinks. It was a place of fun and the odd romance. Every now and then, you would have a youth club disco when all the lads would bring out their best John Travolta *Saturday Night Fever* gear and the girls would get made up and imagine they were Olivia Newton-John or Charlie's Angels.

Mind you, the boys visualised that as well!

We would also have a coach trip away for the day somewhere and we would picnic, play games and generally have a great time.

Also, there was a youth club football team that played against other youth club teams, and also a table tennis team. We won cups in both sports and forged a great team spirit.

I also got my first taste of boxing at a youth club. Nothing official. Just a dusty old box full of old leather lace-up gloves and a bit of tuition from a youth leader. Happy days.

Yes, for some it might seem a little tame compared to hanging out in the park smoking weed, drinking value vodka or pear cider and terrorising old people. But hey, it was more character building.

I went on to help run a youth club in my late teens and enjoyed it immensely. Plus, it was where I met my future wife. The first left hook she landed on me and I knew I was in love forever.

Standards do change considerably.

Back in the day, if you stole apples from somebody's garden, played 'Knockout Ginger' (remember that?) and drank a flagon of Blackthorn cider up the playing fields you were a local hero. Own a GAT gun or air rifle; you were elevated to legendary status.

Now, if you don't have a dozen ASBOs (sorry, out of date now, is it CPIs: Crime Prevention Injunctions?), stole a car, snorted cocaine, had a baby at twelve, shot or stabbed a person, you are nobody.

How times change.

CHAPTER 5

Whatever Happened to
All the Heroes?

I don't know if it's just me but I don't see too many heroes in today's society for kids to aspire to.

In the world of sport... Rooney? Messi? Nadal? Murray? David Haye? Really?

What about TV and film? Ant and Dec? Simon Cowell? Keith Lemon? Graham Norton? Jamie Oliver? Vin Diesel? Jason Statham?

Then there is the world of music... Justin Bieber? JLS? Katy Perry? One Direction?

Not exactly inspiring, is it?

Some of the above are mediocre at best, others talented no doubt, but no charisma, charm or personality worth talking about.

No wonder poor old Michael Parkinson retired from the chat show circuit. I expect he was getting fucking bored to death after having sat and chewed the fat with John Wayne, Fred Astaire, Orson Welles, Bette Davis, Muhammad Ali and of course, Emu!

The '70s, yet again, held host to a multitude of personalities that every youngster wanted to emulate.

This era had three of the biggest global stars on the planet: Elvis Presley, John Lennon and Muhammad Ali. Like them or loathe them, they were known across the universe.

These guys had juggernaut charisma and huge appeal to both males and females.

We had superstar sports personalities. The words 'superstar' and 'world class' are thrown around too easily these days, but who could deny these people the tag: Ali, Pelé, George Best, Bobby Charlton, Bobby Moore, Björn Borg, Ian Botham, Viv Richards, James Hunt, Barry Sheen, Gareth Edwards, Barry John, Brian Jacks, Neil Adams, Martina Navratilova, Billy Jean King, Olga Corbett, Daley Thompson, Seb Coe, Steve Ovett... the list is endless!

What about celebrity sports stars and daredevils like The Harlem Globetrotters basketball team and motorcycle stuntman Evel Knieval?

As mentioned, boxing had the iconic Muhammad Ali at the top of the pile but look at the quality of the challengers to his crown – Joe Frazier, George Foreman, Ken Norton, Ron Lyle, Ernie Shavers. All of them on their day could have been heavyweight champions.

Do Audley Harrison and David Haye come anywhere near to these giants?

But what about the four Kings who battled it out in the late '70s and early '80s? Sugar Ray Leonard, Thomas 'The Hitman' Hearns, Roberto 'Hands of Stone' Duran and 'Marvellous' Marvin Hagler. What warriors. They were always exciting to watch. Boxing no longer has this quality of fighter. They provided mega dollar fights that will go down in the history books for all time. True warriors of the ring.

What about snooker? Once it grew in popularity through the television, it went from a sport being played by middle-aged, Brylcream haired men to flamboyant superstars such as the late great Alex 'Hurricane' Higgins and Jimmy 'Whirlwind' White. Add the pin-up boys like Tony Knowles and Kirk Stevens and the comedy capers of Dennis Taylor and suddenly the sport of snooker became sexy! Everybody suddenly wanted to grab a cue and pot a few balls.

Ian Botham, in the late '70s, made cricket suddenly exciting and interesting, with his gung-ho batting and bowling. He is a true British hero.

What about the brilliant but flawed George Best? In my opinion, the most talented football who ever lived.

We can talk about the Ronaldos and Messis of today but this guy Best was doing things with a football in the '60s and '70s that only others could dream about.

Every boy had pictures of their heroes on their bedroom walls. Along with a few of Charlie's Angels!

The '70s brimmed with heroes from all quarters. We were spoilt beyond belief.

Iconic fictional and real heroes that we wanted to be like.

Who didn't want to be cop heroes such as Starsky and Hutch, Bodie and Doyle, or Regan and Carter? What about other fictional heroes like The A-Team, Buck Rodgers, Dr Who, Wonder Woman, Bionic Man, Bionic Woman, The Man from Atlantis, Thomas Magnum, and The Dukes of Hazzard?

Britain had the hardest men. Police, detectives and secret agents.

Today's TV police are cerebral bores that never draw a gun or punch a villain's teeth out. Not like the men from the past. Who was tougher than Edward Woodward's 'Callan'? A killing machine when needed.

Who can equal the partnership of *The Sweeney's* Jack Ryan and George Carter, played respectively by the late, great John Thaw and the evergreen Dennis Waterman.

These guys days were spent in car chases, busting villains' asses, knocking back whiskey and chatting up 'birds.' What a life.

What about the underestimated talent of Don Henderson in *Bulman* or the granite hard Mark McManus in *Taggart*?

Then we had the tough no nonsense *Hazel* played by Nicolas Ball or Patrick Mower in *Target*.

Great British tough guys.

No crying about man flu or taking a day off work because of a pimple on their ass or a bit of stress.

These men were fucking solid. Not a manbag or a pink t-shirt in sight.

As boys and teenagers, we idolised these people. I am sure there are more that I don't recall but if you had to draw up a list of real heroes today, let's say twenty fictional or real, you would struggle!

No, Jamie Oliver or Russell Brand doesn't qualify.

Forget Wayne Rooney.

Struggling already, eh?

What about Snoop Dog or 50 Cent and their like?

The problem is that these people are only characters. They are not real. They have been manufactured for you to believe that's what they are like. In real life, I suspect they are nothing like their persona.

Which now brings me to the subject of kids strutting around, acting like gangsters. Baseball cap on their head sideways, oversized baseball team shirt, gold chains, trainers with no laces, and worst of all, baggy jeans hanging off of their ass.

I believe the origins of trousers hanging low off your butt came from the American prison system where this was a signal that your ass was available to other prisoners as their bitch, and you were 'showing out' for a pick up!

So it's not fucking cool unless you are cruising for a butt raping. Get a belt and get your trousers up.

As for the chains... people now take the piss out of the stereotypical '70s man with a hairy chest, open shirt, and medallion around his neck. Is it any worse than now when these kids are walking around looking like they have raided their mum's jewellery box? The only cool guy that could get away with this was Mr T, of the A-Team. Who was going to tell him otherwise anyway?

Also, if you are white, stop pretending to be black because you aren't and it doesn't fucking work. Stop being a dick and get your own identity.

Sometimes, the fashion of the '70s left a bit to be desired, but it's got to be better than what we have now.

What about the weasel faced chavs white baseball cap, white Adidas tracky bottoms and Ben Sherman t-Shirt.

Fucking hell. Get some style.

Real men wear leather jackets, Timberland boots, tight black t-shirts, faded jeans and a splash of Hugo Boss. A little face stubble and you are a fucking babe magnet. Oh yes.

I digress slightly...

But what the hell. It needed to be said.

Anyway, back to heroes...

What about the heroes and villains throughout history. The legendary warriors, fighters and men who were men. Will we see their like again?

Tough merciless fighters such as the Vikings, Spartans, Romans, Samurai, Mongol warriors, Apache, Aztecs, Maori, etc. Thank God for the SAS, Navy Seals, Green Berets, Spetsnaz, French Foreign Legion and their like.

Throughout history we have read stories and watched films of the exploits of some incredibly brave people who have become history's heroes. These people were real and went through much adversity to achieve that status. Today some loser wins *Big Brother* or *I'm a Celebrity Get Me Out of Here* and they are nearly elevated to godly status. What utter bollocks.

I remember when a hero was somebody who rowed across the Atlantic single-handedly, not a footballer who scores a winning goal in a match!

Read this list of true men that fought for their country and their beliefs. You would not fuck with them:

- Julius Caesar
- Genghis Khan
- Hannibal
- Lord Nelson
- Alexander the Great
- Napoleon Bonaparte
- Davey Crockett
- Musashi
- William the Conqueror
- William Wallace
- George Patton
- Audie Murphy
- Winston Churchill

History is littered with real men doing what real men do. Brave, strong, courageous, fearless. Isn't that what we men want to be? Not some dithering, soft dope, baking a fucking cake in the kitchen and fretting about his hair gel.

In recent times, the fictional superhero has been brought to the big screen in spectacular CGI fashion. For example: Batman, Spiderman, The X-Men, The Hulk and the awesome Avengers, etc. Brilliant stuff, but don't forget those characters started life in the 1940s.

I grew up on these characters in the Marvel comics. I know the comics are still going strong but most have crap artwork and very few pages, less of a story and twice the price.

Look back at the Silver or Golden Age of these comics and the artwork was superb. The pages would be filled with umpteen panels and dialogue. The comic would take hours to read, not Ten minutes.

These characters were every young man's dream to emulate. The same goes for *Roy of the Rovers* and *Dan Dare.*

Boys comics were boy's comics and girl's comics were girl's comics.

Real boys don't want to read about fashion tips and hair products; they want some kick-ass action going down. Don't they? Please tell me they still do!

Talking of comics, most are overpriced shite these days, aren't they?

Back in the day, you had comics of substance that you could read for days and the Christmas annuals would last you weeks.

They were stuffed full of great stories, pictures, photos, quizzes, and trivia. Yes, here comes a list. Some are also thrown in for the ladies.

Can you remember all these? –

The Eagle, Victor, Hotspur, Hornet, Beano, Dandy, Topper, Beazer, Whizzer and Chips, Roy of the Rovers, Scorcher, Tiger, Cor, Shoot, Commando.

For the ladies – *Jackie, Bunty, Judy, Lookin, Fab 208.*

Great reads, again filled with iconic heroes. Each week, you couldn't wait to read another instalment of what was going on.

Also, the TV screened masses of comic book heroes. Alongside *Batman,* and *Spiderman,* we had *Superman, The Lone Ranger,* and later, *The Thundercats, Masters of The Universe,*

Toxic Crusaders, Ghostbusters, Teenage Mutant Ninja Turtles, Pro-Stars...

These were magical times for me growing up, and later for my kids.

Not a fucking reality programme in sight!

Who is out there now to inspire kids? Who are the manly role models that they should be aspiring to? They are not exactly lining up out there. Why? Because the most powerful media, the television, airs some of the biggest tripe ever put together. Who the fuck runs TV now? Whoever it is hasn't got a clue. If you are not fat, gay, camp, or if you are not physically or mentally deficient, or just plain fucking mad or talentless you will not be on the TV.

My heart bleeds for the likes of Sir David Jason, Dame Helen Mirren and Ray Winstone – all British acting class. Unless they do *I'm a Celebrity Get Me Out of Here* we won't be graced by their presence on the small screen in the near future!

We all need a hero, especially in a time of trouble, worry, or depression; especially with the other crap that is going on in the world.

If the shit hit the fan, who would you call on now to save us?

My top ten 'Real Men' heroes (both real and fictional in no particular order):

- Captain America
- Batman
- Bruce Lee
- Sylvester Stallone
- Chuck Norris
- Spiderman
- Dirty Harry
- Muhammad Ali

- Randy Couture
- Jack Regan

There are many more I could add. Kids just don't read these days. It's all computer games. Their hero is some dead-head that shoots up hookers on *Grand Theft Auto* or the hip hop gangster of the music world. That is all front. Most of them still go home to Mum to have their washing done and go to church on a Sunday. Do you think the massive monster that is the music industry is going to pay real gangsters shed loads of money to fuel their drugs and gun addictions? Get fucking real. It is all hype.

It's the same with people such as Simon Cowell, Lord Sugar and Gordon Ramsey. Do you really think they can say what they want to a person and get away with it? Do you think they are tough guys that don't give a fuck? The only reason they can get away with it, especially Ramsey, is because they have got a dozen cameras and a dozen more security staff around them. Anybody would feel brave when they know they have that safety net to fall back on if somebody really kicked off. It's all television bullshit, hype and propaganda.

These guys are not heroes. They are clever businessmen but that is it.

As a boy TV, film,comics and sport threw up heroes you wanted to aspire to. Men you wanted to be .Here are a few of my favourites. No apologises if some have already been mentioned.

The Fonz, JamesBond, Batman, Kungfu (David Carridine), Starsky and Hutch, Steve Austin (The bionic man).Roy of the Rovers, Muhammad Ali, The man with no name, Lone Ranger, The Incredible Hulk. You get the idea.

Bring back some real heroes with strong morals and ethics. People that want to do right, help others and put themselves second, not fucking first, all the time. People fighting for real causes and not bullshit ones that their agent has made up for them. Like Jamie Oliver's food revolution for schools. How to eat better and educate families on proper nutritional advice. Well, he needs to set a fucking example by losing a few stone before he preaches to others.

Jamie you will have to wait for that fucking knighthood. You need to earn it for a worthy cause, not for boiling a fucking egg or tarting up a few vegetables.

CHAPTER 6

Music for Men

No disrespect to today's music icons but I can't see you around in twenty years time still banging out the hits.

I can't see the youth of today sat hand-in-hand in their seventies saying, "Remember this song, my darling." And then we hear the strangled tones of Pixie Lott, Kanye West or Miley Cyrus.

No timeless classics among that lot.

I can't see them and their like filling stadiums ten or even twenty years from now.

The '70s produced some monster bands that are still kicking naked ass now. Still playing sell-out gigs and embarking on world tours.

Whilst we are on the term band, I am of the understanding that in a band at least three of them play instruments. To me, that is a band.

So this 'boy band' tag is a load of crap. They are groups. They don't play anything. They sing and dance. Or at least, one or possibly two can sing. The rest are fillers.

There are some solid bands around today such as Foo Fighters, Nickelback, Linkin' Park, System of a Down, Disturbed, for example.

The other so they say great bands of today are boys compared to the giants of yesterday.

Can you really stack The Killers, Snow Patrol, Franz Ferdinand or Arctic Monkeys up against the might of The Who,

Rolling Stones, Black Sabbath or Iron Maiden? These guys were/are real rock stars, not just playing at it.

Think of the hardcore bands of yesteryear: The Doors, The Animals, The Kinks, The Beatles, The Stones, The Stooges, Deep Purple, Pink Floyd, Cream, Thin Lizzy, AC/DC, Whitesnake, Bon Jovi, Genesis, Rainbow, Hawkwind, Motörhead, The Eagles, Free, Bad Company, Queen...

Many of these bands are still going now. They are behemoths of their craft, needing a convoy of juggernauts to transport their kit and a private jet to take them from venue to venue.

No namby-pamby stuff here. Real men banging out real tunes. Rock and roll legends that will go down in music history with their place well and truly earned.

Disagree? Then watch the adverts on TV and you will hear umpteen rock classics. Watch the latest films and they are full of big rock anthems, most from yesteryear. Why is that? Because it's real music. It evokes emotion and fist pumping adrenelin. Everybody can't help but sing along to them. Think of *'living on a prayer'* or the *'final countdown'*. They are timeless.

When it comes to iconic rock bands living life in the fast line, with songs about drinking, fighting, sex, drugs and rock 'n' roll, then the three mighty names I am going to put in the frame are Thin Lizzy, AC/DC and Motörhead.

Were there ever three harder, tougher, swaggering renegades?

Lizzy, with their iconic and charismatic front man Phil Lynott, a twinkle in his eye, a cheeky grin, and a silver tongue full of Irish brogue. Dripping classic lines on stage, such as asking the females in the crowd, "Is there anybody out there with any Irish in them?" As a cheer or scream went up, he would learn close to the mic and say, "Is there any of the girls out there who want a little more Irish in them?"

They were the ultimate boys own band with crashing anthems such as 'Jailbreak' and 'The Boys are Back in Town'. Also a host of manly albums such as 'Bad Reputation', 'Fighting', and 'Live and Dangerous'.

Lynott is sadly no longer with us, or the brilliant Gary Moore. Lynott was a throwback to another era. A black Irishman. A poet, a preacher, a fighter, a lover, a drinker, and a brilliant and charismatic front man that had the crowd in the palm of his hands. In my opinion, only the late and great Freddie Mercury of Queen could compare.

What about Australian rockers AC/DC? Dirty guitar riffs, suggestive lyrics and song titles. Angus Young, still hopping around the stage in a schoolboy uniform, and the screaming vocals of the late Bon Scott, and then Brian Johnson. They are one of the biggest rock bands in the world and have been for decades. Stadium fillers, festival headliners and world beaters. Still going strong with their 'all the lads together' anthems such as 'For Those About to Rock (We Salute You)', 'If You Want Blood' and 'Highway to Hell'.

What about those colossal albums with great titles, such as 'High Voltage', 'Back in Black' 'Ballbreaker' 'Razors Edge' and 'Let There Be Rock' Ultimate man music.

What can be said about the third band? The Evergreen Motorhead, led by the gravelly-voiced Lemmy. The man with a face that launched a thousand crying babies. What you see is what you get with Motörhead. Fast, hard thrash rock 'n' roll at its best. How three men can make that much noise, who knows?

Lemmy is probably the greatest living rock singer to have done the whole rock 'n' roll scene to death and back again. One true legend and an enigma to science is how he is still alive.

Classics such as 'Ace of Spades', 'Bomber', and 'Iron Fist' will live in rock history forever. Classic albums like *'No Sleep to Hammersmith'*, *'Inferno'*, *'Iron fist'* and *'Bomber'*. Still a great live act that gives the crowd exactly what they want. Good old rock and roll.

These three bands were, and are, the real deal. Stack them up against Busted, Boyzone or Green Day? You've got to be fucking kidding.

In this day and age, females have enjoyed maybe more chart success than their male counterparts. But to be honest, apart from a couple, the rest are either eye candy or can't sing, full stop.

Now if a female is willing to get in front of the camera with her ass and tits on show, you are guaranteed a smash hit. Singing is secondary to looks. Poor Dusty Springfield must be turning in her grave.

Forget the miracles that can be worked in a recording studio. I am talking about getting out on stage live without backing tracks and backing singers. Most can't.

I believe, in my time, the two most iconic female singers were Debbie Harry of Blondie, and Madonna. The rest are all poor imitations. Honourable mentions to Chrissie Hynde, Kate Bush and Annie Lennox. Todays female vocalist are little girls compared to these women.

The decade of the '70s was indeed a varied and interesting one.

It came in with the last throwbacks of the Sixties psychedelic and prog bands. It went through to glam rock and disco, and then finished with the wild kick-ass explosion of punk music.

We started with Pink Floyd and Cream, experienced Slade, T-Rex and Bowie, boogied to The Bee Gees and Earth, Wind and Fire, and then fried our ears and senses with The Sex Pistols, The Clash and The Stranglers.

What a great time for music!

In amongst it, we had teenybopper mania with The Osmonds, The Jackson 5, David Cassidy and The Bay City Rollers. Plus, the continued chart topping domination of ABBA.

Crazy days.

Days when you actually had to sell shedloads of records to hit the coveted number one spot, and work hard to get air play on Radio 1, bust your ass to be on *Top of the Pops* and take an age to finally churn out a full blooded album.

Today, you can sell between 60,000 and 130,000 records to hit number one. Consider an album such as Queen's *Greatest Hits Vol. 1* has sold to date 5.86 million copies!

Sir Elton John, who is at present celebrating over 40 years in the music industry, is still going strong with a workload that would put singers half his age to shame.

He has, to date, produced thirty studio albums, four live albums, seventeen compilations, three soundtracks, three tribute albums and 128 singles.

The biggest selling single in the UK of all time, 'Candle in the Wind' (1997), has sold, to date, 33 million copies.

His first six albums hit the number one slot in the mighty USA. *'Honky Chateau'*, (1972) went platinum; *'Don't Shoot Me I'm Only the Piano Player'*, (1973) went 3X platinum; *'Goodbye Yellow Brick Road'*, (1973): 7X platinum; *'Caribou'* (1974): 2X platinum; *'Captain Fantastic and the Brown Dirt Cowboy'* (1975): 3X platinum; and *'Rock of Westies'*, (1975): platinum.

Platinum denotes one million sales. Amazing stuff. Who will top that?

What about American rockers KISS and their phenomenal success?

Voted the most popular and most controversial band by teenagers in the USA. Most branded band then and now. Most revolutionary in setting the standards for live gigs. Sold the most tickets. Sold the most merchandise. Have the most fans. Had their own movie. First band to ever debut four solo albums from all four members on the same day. Most popular band of the seventies. Has their brand on just about everything, from condoms to coffins, so you can come and go with the band! Legendary.

This year the phenomenal Beach Boys reformed to do a series of sell out worldwide concerts to celebrate fifty years of their music. Yes, read it again, fifty years. They topped that off with a new album release as well. Fucking awesome!

The bands and artists of yesteryear roll out as monsters of music when it really meant something and not just a quick buck. I am honoured to have been growing up in this era of greats:

- The Beatles
- Rolling Stones
- Led Zeppelin
- Pink Floyd
- The Who
- Bob Dylan
- Eric Clapton
- Jimi Hendrix
- Elton John
- Rod Stewart
- The Doors
- Black Sabbath
- Deep Purple
- The Eagles
- Bee Gees
- Elvis Presley

- Michael Jackson
- Bruce Springsteen
- ABBA
- David Bowie
- Aerosmith
- Iron Maiden
- KISS
- Queen
- Sex Pistols... and so on.

What heavy weights compared to today's lightweights, who have got a job on their hands to manage three hit singles and an album of any substance. Yet, unfortunately today, that is all you need to be shot to mega-stardom and iconic status. What a load of bollocks!

What songs of today will be played over and over, and remain in our hearts and minds forever?

What can compete with classics such as 'Bridge Over Troubled Water', 'Whiter Shade of Pale', 'Nights in White Satin', 'Maggie May', 'Your Song', 'Satisfaction', 'Good Vibrations', 'Hey Jude', 'Hotel California', and 'Bohemian Rhapsody', to name but a few from the golden years.

The world of technology has allowed us the ability to download music straight to our computer. We own it, virtually but not solidly.

I was pissed when cassettes came on the scene and even more baffled when the CD appeared. Marvellous inventions, no doubt, but I loved good old vinyl.

I remember the first 45rpm single I bought: 'Take Me back 'Ome' by Slade, Polydor Records, 1972. With a proper B-side as well, not some shitty megamix or dance version of the A-side. You got value for money.

My first album or LP (longer player on 33rpm) was 'Bolan's Boogie' by the mighty T-Rex.

I shut myself in my parent's front room where they had a radiogram. A large piece of furniture. It was a stylish wood cabinet on legs that held a turntable for records and a MW/LW radio.

I put the record in and followed the lyrics, which were written on the record sleeve.

This is what I miss. The record cover and sleeves on LPs contained a vital mass of information, lyrics, notes, photos and trivia.

Whilst the record played, you could read it over and over again.

The gatefold ones were best. These were usually reserved for a double album, two discs.

The album opened out like a book and contained even more writing, photos, sleeve notes, etc. It was a treasure trove of musical knowledge. A holy grail of lyrical pleasure.

Some of the classic gatefolds I owned were 'Aladdin Sane', David Bowie; 'Goodbye Yellow Brick Road', Elton John; 'Original Soundtrack', 10CC; 'A Night at the Opera', Queen; and 'Live and Dangerous', Thin Lizzy.

The '70s produced some of the biggest selling albums of all time. Legendary vinyl that is timeless.

Here are just a few to remember and revisit:
- Dark Side of the Moon – Pink Floyd
- Led Zeppelin IV – Led Zeppelin
- The Wall – Pink Floyd
- Exile on Main St. – Rolling Stones
- White Album – The Beatles
- Who's Next – The Who
- Blood on the Tracks – Bob Dylan

- Ziggy Stardust – David Bowie
- Born to Run – Bruce Springsteen
- Never Mind the Bollocks – Sex Pistols
- Rumours – Fleetwood Mac
- Rocket to Russia – The Ramones
- Bat out of Hell – Meatloaf
- Billion Dollar Babies – Alice Cooper
- A Night at the Opera – Queen
- Number of the Beast –Iron Maiden
- Boston –Boston
- British Steel – Judas Priest
- Appetite for Destruction – Guns and Roses
- Eliminator – ZZ Top
- Masters of Reality – Black Sabbath
- Paranoid – Black Sabbath
- Machine Head – Deep Purple

This was also the era of the live album. Recorded live in concert. These LPs brought the excitement of a real live gig into the comfort of your living room. They also brought extended versions of some of your best loved tracks and interaction and banter with the crowds. It was the next best thing to being there.

Here again listed are some legendary and classic cuts:
- Made in Japan – Deep Purple
- Rainbow Live on Stage – Rainbow
- Live and Dangerous – Thin Lizzy
- If You Want Blood You've Got It – AC/DC
- Alive I & II – KISS
- Live in the Heart of the City – Whitesnake
- Frampton Comes Alive – Peter Frampton
- Love You Live – Rolling Stones
- Live at Hammersmith – Motorhead

In the Seventies, we also had colour vinyl records and imports from Japan. You were somebody if you owned a limited colour vinyl disc of a popular artist or band.

This era was also the time of the great love songs. Timeless tunes that everybody knows. Songs that are still played today on the radio, as themes to TV programmes or films, and close every party on the dance floors.

Here are a few of the biggest ones:

- I'm Not In Love – 10CC
- Unchained Melody – Righteous Bros
- Your Song – Elton John
- You're in My Heart – Rod Stewart
- Nights in White Satin – Moody Blues
- When I Need You – Leo Sayer
- I Only Have Eyes for You – Art Garfunkel
- I Will Always Love You – Whitney Houston
- (Everything I Do) I Do It For You – Bryan Adams
- Always – Bon Jovi
- I Don't Wanna Miss a Thing – Aerosmith
- Holding Back the Years – Simply Red

I have many happy memories of ending a disco with a few slowies and dancing with the girl of your dreams, your hands slowly sliding down her back to her bum. If they were allowed to stay in place, you quietly smiled and winked at your best mate. Cracked it!

Look at this list of class acts still going strong from the Seventies and Eighties. Monsters of music that dwarf anyone today. Will Pixie Lott, Rihanna or Duffy be banging out tunes to packed stadiums in twenty years time? If so, old Clinton here will wear pink and bake a fucking cake.

Sir Elton John, Bruce Springsteen, Rod Stewart, Sir Tom Jones, Tom Petty, U2, Bon Jovi, Rolling Stones, The Who.

David Bowie, Sir Paul McCartney, Bryan Adams, Iggy Pop, Black Sabbath, Deep Purple, Def Leppard, Whitesnake, Billy Joel, Neil Diamond, Eric Clapton, Pink Floyd, Queen, Motorhead, Iron Maiden, AC/DC... the list goes on.

What about the musical legends we lost?

Pure genius, never to be seen again:

Elvis Presley, John Lennon, Marc Bolan, Freddie Mercury, Phil Lynott, Jimi Hendrix, Bob Marley, Kurt Cobain, Michael Jackson, The Ramones, Gary Moore, Joe Strummer, Jim Morrison, Buddy Holly, Roy Orbison to name a few.

A different class all together. Real men like loud music. No dance shit or R&B bollocks. REAL MEN want loud music thrashed out on an electric guitar. YES! You want to come out of a live gig being deaf for at least three days. You want music to get the adrenalin pumping and the blood flowing, not to put you to fucking sleep. Rock and roll is music for men in whatever form. It is THE music in my opinion. Everything else isn't real. Real bands have axe legends that can play a guitar to death even under water or on the moon. They sleep with their guitars and make love to them. Real bands have charismatic lead singers whose voices can vibrate around an open air arena effortlessly, with a god given manliness. The real bands have men in not boys who haven't yet taken their first shave and whose balls haven't dropped.

As AC/DC sang, 'For those about to rock, we salute you!'

Footnote: As I write this the legendary Rolling Stones have just kicked off their centenary year tour at London's O2 arena. All of them touching seventy and still kicking ass. Great to see and an example to all wannabe rock bands.

CHAPTER 7

Man Movies

I love films and going to the cinema. There are some great films around today but most now rely on computer generated visual effects or animation over well-known actors starring in films.

You can count worthy modern day actors and actresses on one hand. DiCaprio, Cruise, Bale, Pitt, Butler, Sutherland, Crowe. Who is carrying the flag for the action heroes? Vin Diesel? The Rock? Not exactly inspiring stuff, is it?

In the '70s and '80s, you had the acting might of Burton, Harris, O'Toole, Wayne, Eastwood, Bronson, Reynolds, Newman, McQueen, De Niro, Pacino, Hopkins, Nicholson, Hackman, Reed, Finney, Bates, Sutherland, Marvin, Hoffman, Streep, Foster, Weaver, Caine, Douglas, Connery, Moore... the list is endless.

Action heroes? The holy trinity of Stallone, Schwarzenegger and Willis.

What about Bruce Lee, Chuck Norris, the evergreen Jackie Chan, Dolph Lundgren, and later Van-Damme and Seagal. What a line-up that you wouldn't want to piss off.

When you went to the cinema, more often than not, you saw two films back to back. You'd be in there four hours or more.

What about the all-night martial arts or horror marathons of five or six films? Go in at 11:00 at night and come out at 7:30 the following morning. Bring a haversack full of grub and drink and you thought you were on your holidays.

You would eventually stumble out of the cinema into the early morning light, after happily satisfying all your bloodthirsty, barbaric, and totally violent urges. Wonderful stuff.

Now I know that recent times have spawned some epic films, such as *The Lord of the Rings* and the *Harry Potter* franchise. *Inception* was awesome. The big Marvel and DC comic book films are up there. But then many others pass us by with mediocrity or a plot that, for a person of my age, you have seen before. Or a remake that is not a patch on the original.

Yes, here comes another list of blockbuster epics and cult classics from my era:

Jaws, Earthquake, The Towering Inferno, Taxi Driver, The Magnificent Seven, The Godfather, The Dirty Dozen, Easy Rider, Marathon Man, The French Connection I and II, The Exorcist, The Omen, Deliverance, Shaft, The Poseidon Adventure, Apocalypse Now, Saturday Night Fever, Butch Cassidy and The Sundance Kid, James Bond (take your pick!), *Where Eagles Dare, The Good, The Bad and The Ugly, Star Wars, One Flew Over the Cuckoo's Nest, Silence of the Lambs, Dirty Dancing...*

Cult classics included:

Dirty Harry, Death Wish, Freebie and the Bean, Enter the Dragon, Last Tango in Paris, The Deer-hunter, Rollerball, The Texas Chainsaw Massacre, Halloween, Friday the 13th, First Blood, The Shining, Scarface, The Terminator, Die Hard, Planet of the Apes... Ah, I'm going mad! There's just so many!

These big films also starred big names. Charismatic, tough, strong characters. I defy any real man not to get pumped up at any of the Stallone *Rocky* fights, or get a surge of adrenaline when he is training and runs up the seventy-two steps of the Philadelphia Museum of Art.

What about Eastwood's icon cop Dirty Harry pointing that .44 Magnum in some lowlife's face and uttering the immortal words, "Go ahead, make my day."

It never fails to make me grin knowingly as if to say, "Yeah, let him have it!"

I think one of the most intense and stirring screen moments in recent times was the face to face sit-down conversation between screen legends Robert De Niro and Al Pacino in the film *Heat*. If you haven't seen this, do so to witness a master class in acting!

On the same note, what about Jack Nicholson's performance in *The Shining*? Whenever I watch this film it still evokes fear and uneasiness, mainly due to Nicholson's chilling portrayal of family man Jack Torrence slipping into madness.

Who can't resist a smile and a fist pump at John Rambo running amok with a M16 or Schwarzenegger's Terminator relentlessly hunting down his victims?

Then, we have the action packed antics of Bruce Willis' John McClane in the *Die Hard* franchise, still going now. Didn't every man at one stage secretly want to be running around in a bloodstained vest, a couple of guns in his hands, and shooting the bad guys?

These images of cinematic, tough guy action heroes are seared into my subconscious. In my opinion, they have not been beaten and never will be.

The '70s and '80s were definitely the time of the action hero. I bet every 50+ male waited in rabid anticipation when Stallone announced he was resurrecting Rocky Balboa and John Rambo in recent years, and probably near pissed their pants when *The Expendables* was released with the Holy Trinity of Stallone, Willis and Schwarzenegger united on screen.

As I am writing, *The Expendables 2* is in production. Magic.

If not, you are not a real man. You are a pretender.

Watching Owen Wilson or Jim Carrey prancing around desperately looking for laughs isn't going to cut it, buddy.

Yes, I will agree that the Holy Trinity did make some shit films in between their classics, but they still hold a screen presence that few do today.

These guys prided themselves on being in most of the film themselves, and did most of their own stunts. They always looked cool, even running around covered in blood, sweat, dirt, and some bad guy's brains all over them.

Could there ever have been a cooler hero than Richard Rowntree's Shaft? He always looked good, even when punching out a dozen hard men.

Bond is super cool. Sometimes shaken but never stirred!

Who can equal the screen presences of hell-raisers like Burton, Harris, O'Toole or Reed? Men you didn't fuck with in real life.

They weren't worried about moisturisers, shaped eyebrows or fake tans. They were just worried about acting, hunting down the next drink, and good looking woman!

These guys were not pretty-boy actors more worried about their hair than delivering the goods. These were rugged, screen gods. They may not have been blessed with the looks of Clooney or Pitt, but that didn't stop them having a legion of female admirers.

So, raise a glass and salute the granite-hard features of Robert Mitchum, Lee Marvin and Charles Bronson.

These guys are irreplaceable. They were monsters of the screen. But then, going back even further, they had names such as Dean, Bogart, Cagney, and Gable to aspire to.

In this day and age, many of cinema's heroes are computer generated cartoon characters, not real people.

The 70's and 80's were the time of 'real men movies.' Men like action movies, cool heroes that can fight, shoot and get the girl.

My favourite action films of that era:
- *Die Hard* – Bruce Willis
- *Dirty Harry* – Clint Eastwood
- *Death Wish* – Charles Bronson
- *Rambo: First Blood* – Sylvester Stallone
- *The Terminator* – Arnold Schwarzenegger

My top ten tough guys from that era, (again in no particular order):
- Clint Eastwood
- Charles Bronson
- Sylvester Stallone
- Arnold Schwarzenegger
- Bruce Willis
- Chuck Norris
- Dolph Lundgren
- Steven Seagel
- Burt Reynolds
- Richard Rowntree

Top ten men that men don't mind:

Previous guys are all in there. But what about the men that played the occasional romantic role that didn't compromise their manliness:
- Jeff Bridges
- Kurt Russell
- Kevin Costner
- Michael Douglas
- Richard Gere
- Harrison Ford
- Mel Gibson

- Don Johnson
- Dennis Quaid
- Patrick Swayze

Yeah, they did alright. Nothing wrong with a man being a gentleman. It's okay to be sensitive now and again, or even shed a tear if it's for a worthy cause. Not because you lost your fucking pink shirt, burnt your soufflé, or watched your favourite Disney film.

That's not on.

Clinton's quick film quiz

See if you can remember what films these classic lines come from. Give yourself two points for a correct answer. Get them all right you are a real man! No cheating.

1. 'I love the smell of napalm in the morning!'
2. 'I think we're going to need a bigger boat!'
3. 'Yo Adrian! I did it!'
4. 'Boards don't hit back!'
5. 'You've got to ask yourself a question: Do I feel lucky? Well, do you, punk?!'
6. 'I'll make him an offer he can't refuse'
7. 'Are you talking to me?'
8. '*Hasta la vista* baby'
9. 'It was the bogey man, wasn't it?'/'As a matter of fact it was.'
10. 'Leave it or I'll give you a war you'll never believe'.

Answers:

1. *Apocalypse Now*
2. *Jaws*
3. *Rocky*
4. *Enter the Dragon*
5. *Dirty Harry*
6. *The Godfather*
7. *Taxi driver*
8. *The Terminator*
9. *Halloween*
10. *Rambo*

CHAPTER 8

TV for Tough Guys

In this day and age, we can get literally hundreds of TV channels. You can flip aimlessly for ten minutes or more looking at them.

I come from an era where I remember initially having three channels and they didn't actually start to broadcast until early evening. No daytime TV here, my little square-eyed friends.

We didn't have the pleasure (or displeasure, depending on how you view it) of seeing the likes of Eamonn Holmes, Lorraine Kelly, Paul O'Grady, Alan Titchmarsh, Richard and Judy, or Philip Schofield, Jeremy Kyle, or the Loose Women. God, what a fucking empty space there was in my life!

When you viewed the television back then, you had to be patient, as it took five minutes to warm up and come on. But hey, it was worth the wait.

Those three channels had far better programmes on them than the multitude we have today. How some of the total and utter shit that passes for a programme gets commissioned is beyond me.

Who the hell wants to see programmes with titles like, 'My Exploding Tits', 'I'm a Fat Bastard and Need to Lose Weight' 'Tortoise Rescue', 'My Mother-in-law is a Pole Dancer', 'Toilet Cleaners of Edinburgh', and mind-numbing hours of cookery, housing, and antiques programmes. Give me a break!

I'd rather pull my teeth out with a pair of pliers, or nail my testicles to the dining room table.

Back in the day, the TV exploded with stars. They were lining up to be on our screens.

There were no video or DVD recorders then, no Sky+. But if there was, you would have been recording all week. In fact, you wouldn't have bothered leaving the house. Telly was too good. Seriously, it was.

Here is a taste of what you got every week. You just didn't know how lucky you were:

The Sweeney, Minder, Magnum, The A Team, Knight Rider, MASH, Fawlty Towers, Blackadder, Top of The Pops, Tomorrow's World, World in Action, Generation Game, Golden Shot, Sunday Night at the London Palladium, Morecombe & Wise Show, The Two Ronnies, Callan, Columbo, Starsky and Hutch, Kojak, Kung Fu, The Waltons, Goodies, That's Life, Streets of San Francisco, Dallas, Parkinson, It's a Knockout, Seaside Special, Monty Python, Man about the House, The Comedians, Opportunity Knocks, Take your Pick, Sale of the Century, Randall & Hopkins, Dr Who, This Is Your Life, Lost in Space, Thriller, Tales of the Unexpected, The Saint, The Avengers, The Champions, The Persuaders, Department S, McMillan & Wife, McCloud, the Carry On films...

Later we had:

Russ Abbott's Madhouse, Noel's House Party, The Professionals, Auf Weidersehen Pet, TJ Hooker, The Young Ones, Celebrity Squares, Pop Quiz, Baywatch, Prime Suspect, Dempsey & Makepiece, The Equalizer, Only Fools and Horses, Lovejoy, London's Burning...

It just goes on. All TV gold.

Kids' programmes were in their abundance. There were some great wacky, zany and extremely funny ones like *Tiswas, Multicoloured Swap Shop* and the *Banana Splits.*

Classics such as *Sooty, Basil Brush, Trumpton, The Flowerpot Men, Scooby Doo, The Tomorrow People, The Magic Roundabout,*

Wacky Races, *Top Cat*, *The Flintstones*, *Thunderbirds*, *Captain Scarlet*, *Happy Days*, *Mork and Mindy* and *Crackerjack*, to name a few...

TV series lasted twelve or sixteen episodes, not six. Christmas specials were brilliant, chocked full of stars. Big films. Pure entertainment. Noel Edmond's at a children's hospital. *Christmas Top of the Pops*. Not a fucking reality programme in sight. Not one sign of a bunch of useless, talentless twats that you wouldn't piss on if they were on fire.

Those were the days when the people who ran television knew what the public wanted. Today's TV executives wouldn't know a good programme if it ran up and kicked them in the balls.

Yes, there are still a few good programmes that crop up now and again such as *Harry Hill*, *Ant and Dec*, *Peter Kay*, *A Touch of Frost* or *Lewis*. But these are few and far between compared to the other shite that gets air time.

Where's the big names? Remember these characters?

Regan and Carter, Starsky and Hutch, Thomas Magnum, The Fonz, BA Baracus, Michael Knight, Steve Austin, The Saint, Basil Fawlty, Yosser Hughes, Oz, Captain Kirk and Spock, Phantom Flan Flinger, Bernie the Bolt, Bully, Arthur Daley, DCI Tennison from Prime Suspect, Skippy, The Wombles, Buck Rodgers, Joe 90, Dick Dastardly and Muttley, Bodie and Doyle, Ironside, JR Ewing, The Green Cross Code Man, Andy Pandy, Flowerpot Men, Florence, Zebedee and Dougal of The Magic Roundabout, Top Cat, Dusty Bin, Del Boy and Rodney.

What about those iconic film heroes then? What a line-up... Rambo, Rocky Balboa, Harry Callaghan, Terminator, Hans Solo, Darth Vader, Luke Skywalker, Michael Myers, Leatherface, Jason Vorhees, Freddie Krueger, Hannibal Lecter, Tony

Moreno, Don Corleone, John McClane, Ellen Ripley, 'Popeye' Doyle, Quint, Sarah Connor, Norman Bates and James Bond.

Quite a list?

How many iconic characters are about in film and TV today?

Not many I think.

It's a crying shame that TV does not commission such British acting class to be on our small screens more.

Ray Winstone, Robert Carlyle, Sean Bean, Sean Pertwee, Ken Stott, Robbie Coltrane, Phillip Glenister, John Simm, Dame Helen Mirren, to name but a few.

They are criminally under-used or ignored in favour of total wastes of space like Jedward and their reality contempories.

Where have all the great dramas and comedy shows gone? Now when a decent two-part drama comes along or a one-off special of the brilliant *A Touch of Frost*, we see spoiler clips for a month leading up to it as if it was a world event. Back in my day, it was just another night on the telly.

I have just recently watched the new series of *Dallas*. The new cast are doing a great job, but 84 year-old Larry Hagman, a.k.a JR Ewing, is immense. He is a still a giant with the screen presence to make you believe he really is the clever, conniving, and ruthless oil tycoon. Can there possibly be a more famous TV baddie ever? Every time he is on the screen, it is an acting master class. Hagman and his like will never be replaced. They are acting gold. The young pretenders fall in his wake.

These guys brought real entertainment into your living room.

(As I write this, Larry Hagman has sadly passed away. A tragic loss. There will only ever be one JR Ewing).

What about the comedy giants that graced our screens, bringing us laughter every week? Morecombe and Wise, The

Two Ronnies, Bob Monkhouse, Kenny Everett, Freddie Starr, Jimmy Tarbuck, Benny Hill and Larry Grayson.

Then there were the classic sitcoms: *The Good Life*, *Fawlty Towers*, *Porridge*, *Steptoe and Son*, the brilliant Michael Crawford in *Some Mothers Do Ave Em'*, *Rising Damp*, *On the Buses*, *The Likely Lads*, *The Liver Birds*, *Man About the House*, *Citizen Smith*, *It Ain't Half Hot Mum*, *Dad's Army*.

Later came the brilliant *Blackadder* and *Only Fools and Horses*.

The list is endless.

The only three sitcoms of recent times that earn mention in the same breath are, in my opinion, *Father Ted*, *The Vicar of Dibley* and *Phoenix Nights*. There are no sitcoms of any worth these days and no big name comedians to star in them.

I can't understand why people want to waste their lives and brain cells watching the morning time debate or chat shows. If I wanted to watch a bunch of brain dead freaks or gobby self-opinionated women, I could go down my local pub.

What the fuck is *Big Brother* all about? People sat up all night watching somebody sleep when they should be asleep. "Oh look he snored", or "She flashed a partial boob", or "He farted". Big fucking deal. Get a life.

I would love Rambo to run into the Big Brother house armed to the teeth with grenades, an M16, and a flamethrower, and put the fuckers out of their misery.

Then we have *The X-Factor*. Okay, some talent has been unearthed; Leona Lewis, for example. But does this show really have to run from August to December? That is overkill. Especially having to look at Louis Walsh's grinning face on the judge's panel, talking a load of bollocks and voting for talentless freaks to stay in the show!

Britain's Got Talent – it's a great idea, but the eventual winners have no TV vehicle to make themselves household names.

Not like the old school talent shows like *Opportunity Knocks* and *New Faces*. These shows spawned some of Britain's best talent who went on to have their own shows.

Opportunity Knocks made household names and stars out of names such as Freddie Starr, Paul Daniels, Frank Carson, Pam Ayres, and Lena Zavaroni.

Some of *New Faces* winners were Lenny Henry, Marti Caine, Michael Barrymore, Victoria Wood, Les Dennis, and Jim Davison.

Most of these stars went on to have their own shows or be regular guests on others.

Now, the best the winners can hope for after is a one spot on the Royal Variety Performance or a summer gig at Butlins! Then, it is a quick downward slide to the local community centre's Saturday knees up. Whoopee!

Bring back *Sunday Night at the Palladium* and give some of these talented people a vehicle to showcase their skills more easily. Get Peter Kay to host it and get some big headline talents to top the bill. Do it weekly, not once a year.

The success of *Britain's Got Talent*, should tell TV bosses that we still like and want variety shows on our screens. Otherwise, the people that are held in high esteem in the variety world, like the Forsythes, Monkhouses, Corbetts, would not be the megastar household names they are today.

TV, man up and bring back the variety now!

No, we don't want another 'I'm *Dancing on Ice*, cum *X-Factor*, cum *Pop Star to Opera Star*' shit. I've had enough of seeing third-rate celebrities trying to resurrect their dead careers by eating kangaroo testicles or showing off their tits. I don't want to see another Gordon Ramsey programme either where he is pretending to be a tough guy. If he wasn't surrounded by a dozen cameras and a dozen more security guards, he wouldn't say boo to a goose even if he had cooked the bastard!

The same goes for Jeremy Kyle. Outside the confines of the studio he would get the crap beat out of him for mouthing off the way he does. (Jerry Springer did it bigger and better!)

Save us, please, from any more of this bollocks and let's get some real TV back, with real actors and people that we really care about.

Shows such as *Columbo* with the brilliant Peter Falk as the crumpled but genius detective, had the stars of the day queuing up.

Here is a selection:

Ray Milland, Dick Van Dyke, Jack Cassidy, Faye Dunaway, Patrick McGoohan ,William Shatner, Donald Pleasance, Robert Vaughn and Lawrence Harvey.

These people were, in their own right, acting giants, but they all wanted to play the role of the murderer alongside Peter Falk. It's amazing that they were all on the small screen.

The same can be said for the early Eighties show *Lovejoy*, starring the brilliant Ian McShane in the title role as the lovable rogue antique dealer.

Stars such as Joanna Lumley, Linda Grey, Tom Wilkinson, Richard Briers, Anthony Valentine, Frank Windsor, Larry Lamb and Brian Blessed were on the show. Television wouldn't commission that now or pay the wages.

But they will effortlessly commission pure mind-numbing rubbish. The fucking dregs of life in these shows wouldn't get the time of day down the local dole office, let alone be unleashed on the television. We want real programmes and real stars with talent, charisma, charm, intelligence and acting ability. Not some moron who has got a job on his hands just to remember their own name, thinks the capital of England is 'E', and couldn't find their ass even with both their hands.

Do the TV executives think all of the great British public are fucking morons!?

*

The adverts were always a great source of entertainment and I think many still are today. Sometimes, they are more entertaining than the programmes themselves. (Not a hard feat to accomplish!)

If you are a child of the '70s, see if you recall this little lot: The Nimble Bread Girl in a balloon, The Robot Aliens for Cadbury's Smash, Hiy Karate aftershave, The Flake Girl, Shake 'n' Vac, Brut Splash It All Over, The Milk Tray Man, The Gold Blend Couple, Joan Collins and Leonard Rossitter in the Cinzano adverts, Rowan Atkinson in the Barclayclay's adverts, 'Go to work on an egg', Typhoo Chimps, Honey Monster, Condor Moment Cigar advert, Old Spice Surfer, Pick Up a Penguin, 'Watch out watch out, there's a Humphrey about' (Milk ad), and Clunk Click Every Trip.

Great stuff.

They were an entertaining break between a classic TV programme and not the main fucking event as they are today.

Also adverts weren't on your screen relentlessly every five minutes or so. In the end, it´s like a Chinese water torture over the duration of a sixty or ninety minute programme.

Back in the day, a sixty minute programme would probably be around fifty three minutes minus seven for adverts. Now, a sixty minute programme runs about forty five minutes with about fifteen minutes for adverts. That's insane.

What about these mini spoilers for up and coming programmes? Does that piss you off or what? How many times can you see the same clip repeated and repeated until you lose the will to live?

Also, don't you find the clip they continually play is the best bit of the programme anyway? No need to sit through the rest of the shite.

My advice is searching your digital channels for TV Gold and enjoy some real television.

Here is an A to Z list of classic UK television programmes. See how many you remember and how good they were.

A

- *A Day with Dana*
- *Ace of Wands*
- *The Adventures of Rupert Bear*
- *Agony*
- *Albert and Victoria*
- *Alcock and Gander*
- *Alexander the Greatest*
- *All Creatures Great and Small*
- *All Gas and Gaiters*
- *All Our Saturdays*
- *Alright Now*
- *...And Mother Makes Five*
- *...And Mother Makes Three*
- *Angels*
- *Animal Kwackers*
- *Anne of Avonlea*
- *Antiques Roadshow*
- *Apaches*
- *Aquarius*

- *Are You Being Served?*
- *Arena*
- *Armchair Theatre*
- *Armchair Thriller*
- *Arthur of the Britons*

B
- *Bachelor Father*
- *Backs to the Land*
- *Bagpuss*
- *Ballet Shoes*
- *Barlow at Large*
- *The Bass Player and the Blonde*
- *The Benny Hill Show*
- *Beryl's Lot*
- *The Black and White Minstrel Show*
- *Blake's 7*
- *Blankety Blank*
- *Bleep and Booster*
- *Bless Me Father*
- *Bless This House*
- *Bloomers*
- *Blue Peter*
- *Blue Peter Special Assignment*
- *The Book Tower*
- *Bouquet of Barbed Wire*
- *Bowler*
- *The Brothers*
- *Budgie*
- *A Bunch of Fives*
- *Butterflies*

C

- *Call My Bluff*
- *Callan*
- *Carrie's War*
- *Carry On Laughing*
- *The Cedar Tree*
- *The Changes*
- *Check It Out*
- *Cheggers Plays Pop*
- *The Chinese Puzzle*
- *Churchill's People*
- *Citizen Smith*
- *Clangers*
- *A Class by Himself*
- *Codename*
- *Come Back Mrs. Noah*
- *The Comedians*
- *Comedy Playhouse*
- *Coronation Street*
- *Crackerjack*
- *Cribb*
- *Crossroads*
- *Crown Court*
- *The Cuckoo Waltz*

D

- *Dad's Army*
- *Danger UXB*
- *Department S*
- *The Devil's Crown*
- *Dick Barton*
- *Dickens of London*

- *Dixon of Dock Green*
- *Doctor at Large*
- *Doctor at Sea*
- *Doctor in Charge*
- *Doctor in the House*
- *Doctor on the Go*
- *Doctor Who*
- *The Doctors*
- *Don't Ask Me*
- *Don't Drink the Water*
- *Dr. Finlay's Casebook*
- *The Duchess of Duke Street*
- *The Dustbinmen*

E

- *Edward & Mrs. Simpson*
- *Edward the Seventh*
- *Emmerdale*
- *Emu's TV Series*
- *End of Part One*
- *Everyman*

F

- *The Fall and Rise of Reginald Perrin*
- *A Family at War*
- *The Family*
- *The Famous Five*
- *Father Brown*
- *Father, Dear Father*
- *Fawlty Towers*
- *The Fenn Street Gang*
- *The Film programme*

- *Flambards*
- *The Flaxton Boys*
- *The Flockton Flyer*
- *Follyfoot*
- *The Fosters*
- *Freewheelers*
- *Friday Night, Saturday Morning*
- *From a Bird's Eye View*

G

- *Gangsters*
- *Gardeners' World*
- *General Hospital*
- *The Generation Game*
- *George and Mildred*
- *The Georgian House*
- *Get It Together*
- *The Good Life*
- *The Good Old Days*
- *The Goodies*
- *Graham's Gang*
- *Grandstand*
- *Grange Hill*

H

- *Heart of the Matter*
- *Holiday*
- *Horizon*
- *How*

I

- *I Didn't Know You Cared*
- *I, Claudius*
- *In Loving Memory*
- *International Mastermind*
- *It Ain't Half Hot Mum*
- *It'll be Alright on the Night*
- *ITV Playhouse*

J

- *Jamie and the Magic Torch*
- *Jason King*
- *Jazz 625*
- *Jigsaw*
- *The Julie Andrews Hour*
- *Just William*
- *Justice*

K

- *Kate*
- *The Kids from 47A*
- *The Krypton Factor*

L

- *Landward*
- *Last of the Summer Wine*
- *Late Night Line-Up*
- *Leap in the Dark*
- *The Legend of Robin Hood*
- *Life on Earth*
- *Lift Off with Ayshea*
- *Lillie*

- *List of Ripping Yarns episodes*
- *The Liver Birds*
- *Lizzie Dripping*
- *The Losers*
- *The Love School*
- *Love Thy Neighbour*
- *The Lovers*

M

- *The Main Chance*
- *The Mallens*
- *Man About the House*
- *Man at the Top*
- *Manhunt*
- *Marked Personal*
- *The Marty Feldman Comedy Machine*
- *Mastermind*
- *Match of the Day*
- *Me Mammy*
- *The Mind Beyond*
- *Mind Your Language*
- *Minder*
- *The Misfit*
- *Monty Python's Flying Circus*
- *The Moon Stallion*
- *Moonbase 3*
- *Mr. and Mrs.*
- *Multi-Coloured Swap Shop*
- *Music Time*
- *My Old Man*
- *Mystery and Imagination*

N

- *Name That Tune*
- *Napoleon and Love*
- *Natural World*
- *Nearest and Dearest*
- *The Nearly Man*
- *Never Mind the Quality, Feel the Width*
- *The New Avengers*
- *New Faces*
- *New Scotland Yard*
- *Newsround*
- *No – That's Me Over Here!*
- *No, Honestly*
- *Not On Your Nellie*
- *Not Only... But Also*
- *Not the Nine O'Clock News*
- *Now Look Here*

O

- *Odd Man Out*
- *Oh No, It's Selwyn Froggitt!*
- *Oh, Brother!*
- *Oil Strike North*
- *The Omega Factor*
- *Omnibus*
- *On the Buses*
- *The Onedin Line*
- *Only When I Laugh*
- *Open All Hours*
- *Opportunity Knocks*
- *Orson Welles' Great Mysteries*
- *Our Mutual Friend*

P

- *The Pallisers*
- *Panorama*
- *Pardon My Genie*
- *Parkinson*
- *Pathfinders*
- *Paul Temple*
- *Pebble Mill at One*
- *The Persuaders!*
- *Pipkins*
- *Play Away*
- *Play for Today*
- *Please Sir!*
- *Points of View*
- *Poldark*
- *Porridge*
- *Prince Regent*
- *The Protectors*
- *Public Eye*

Q

- *Q*
- *Queenie's Castle*
- *A Question of Sport*
- *Question Time*
- *Quiller*

R

- *The Rag Trade*
- *Rainbow*
- *Randall and Hopkirk*
- *Rentaghost*

- *Return of the Saint*
- *Revolver*
- *Ripping Yarns*
- *Rising Damp*
- *Robin's Nest*
- *Rock Goes to College*
- *Roobarb*
- *Rosie*
- *Rumpole of the Bailey*
- *Runaround*
- *Rutland Weekend Television*

S

- *Sale of the Century*
- *Saturday Banana*
- *Scene*
- *Score with the Scaffold*
- *Screen Test*
- *Second Verdict*
- *Secret Army*
- *The Secret War*
- *Shades of Greene*
- *A Sharp Intake of Breath*
- *Shelley*
- *The Siege of Golden Hill*
- *Ski Sunday*
- *The Sky at Night*
- *The Sky's the Limit*
- *Softly, Softly: Taskforce*
- *Some Mothers Do 'Ave 'Em*
- *Something Else*
- *The Sooty Show*

- *The South Bank Show*
- *South Today*
- *Space: 1999*
- *Spotlight*
- *The Standard*
- *Star Maidens*
- *The Stars Look Down*
- *State of the Nation*
- *Steptoe and Son*
- *Strangers*
- *Sunday Night at the London Palladium*
- *Supernatural*
- *Survival*
- *Survivors*
- *The Sweeney*
- *Sykes*
- *Sykes and a Big, Big Show*

T

- *Take Three Girls*
- *Tales of the Unexpected*
- *Terry and June*

Well, how many do you remember? Make a top ten out of them for yourself. How many reality shows did you find? How many big name actors can you remember in these shows? Note also that this is just UK shows. This does not include the US imports that flooded our screens at this time as well.

Massive US shows such as MASH, Alias Smith and Jones, The Waltons, Hawaii Five O, Kojak, Dallas, Starsky and Hutch and Magnum P.I. to name but a few. Classic TV never to be seen again... unless you buy the boxset of course. Thank God for Amazon!

CHAPTER 9

Legends of Yesteryear

When I was a boy, there was a programme on the television every week called *This is Your Life*. It went through various presenters over the years, but the theme stayed the same. A solid half hour of a show where a celebrity, sportsperson or unsung hero would unexpectedly have their life story laid out in front of them.

It was great television to get a glimpse into their private lives, see their friends and family, and hear some great anecdotes.

Here is a list of some of the famous people that were on the show:

Muhammad Ali, Bobby Charlton, Billy Connelly, Dame Shirley Bassey, George Best, Ian Botham, Bob Geldof, Les Dawson, Ken Dodd, Diana Dors, Richard Harris, Bob Hope, David Frost, Frankie Howard, Bob Monkhouse, Christopher Lee, Omar Sharif, Oliver Reed, Eric Sykes, Alan Whicker, Barbara Windsor, Edward Woodward...

What a mighty line-up.

Also, we had the legendary chat-show *Parkinson*. It was unique in the fact that the interviewer, Parkinson, was actually interested in his guests and not using the show as a vehicle to show what an amazingly funny, zany, sharp guy he was.

So different from today's so-called chat show hosts.

Parkinson met and interviewed the biggest and finest stars of their time, true icons, and people who could wear the tag 'legend'. Here is listed some of the best he had on the show:

Bing Crosby, Muhammad Ali, Michael Caine, Sean Connery, Jack Nicholson, Orson Welles, John Wayne, Bette Davis, Oliver Reed, Joan Collins, John Lennon, Sir Elton John, Madonna, Paul McCartney, Anthony Hopkins, David Beckham, Tony Blair, Tommy Cooper, Clint Eastwood, James Cagney, Robert Mitchum, Peter Sellers and David Niven. And let's not forget Rod Hull and Emu.

What a fantastic honour and experience it is to sit and talk with these people.

I often think if either or both shows came back to television we would struggle to find people of this calibre to fill these chairs and enthral us.

Who would you have? Eh?

Wayne Rooney? Katie Price? Peter Andre? Jamie Oliver? Wagner? What a joke. I would rather watch a blank screen.

If you were going to host a *Come Dine With Me* special, who would you invite to sit around your table to share a meal and good conversation?

You are allowed four guests. They can be living or dead heroes that you invite. Who would it be? Tough one, isn't it?

After a lot of thought, here is my four:

1. Bruce Lee – the legendary martial arts master was my hero and inspiration growing up, and he inspired me to take up martial arts, which has become a major part of my life

2. Bob Monkhouse – an incredibly witty and knowledgeable man. A mind of information, trivia and stories. A true comic genius.

3. Clint Eastwood – a screen god. A true living legend. Dirty Harry at your dinner table. Enough said punk.

4. Dame Helen Mirren – I wanted to choose a female to complement the three males. I can't think of anyone better; a beautiful, strong, witty, intelligent woman that could hold

her own in any male dominated environment and be totally captivating.

So what's your line-up and why?

Yes, earlier on I mentioned that I hated reality shows. But I would love to put the following people in the jungle for *I'm a Celebrity Get Me Out of Here'*

This line-up would make a great show, better than the third raters that are in it at present:

Simon Cowell, Paul Gascoigne, Piers Morgan, Ray Winstone, Holly Willoughby, Cheryl Cole, Dale Winton, Mr T, Richard & Judy, and Jamie Oliver.

What a diverse line-up. What a show. Now that would be riveting television. TV executives pay the money and let's see it!

On another note, imagine having a drink down the pub with these lads: Oliver Reed, Richard Burton, Richard Harris, Jack Nicholson, Keith Moon and George Best.

A good night was had by all, and a good day, and another good night, etc. etc.

Or what about celebrating St Patrick's Day by partying with Phil Lynott, Alex Higgins, George Best. Bob Geldof, Colin Farrell and Dermot Morgan (*Father Ted*).

So many legendary screen and television icons have gone to their graves. From Dean, Monroe, Burton, Brando, to Michael Jackson, Alex Higgins, Bestie, and Oliver Reed. Great comedians and entertainers such as Ronnie Barker, Morecombe and Wise, Les Dawson, Benny Hill and Bob Monkhouse.

One man who seems to stay evergreen is all round entertainer, Sir Bruce Forsyth. At the time of writing, he is 83 years young. He has had seventy — yes, seventy — years in show business, and has seen and done it all.

He is a national treasure. He was knighted recently for services rendered, and quite rightly so. Whilst others have fallen, Sir Bruce keeps rolling on, and long may he do so.

Along with other national treasures such as Sir Tom Jones and Sir Elton John, these guys are the true legends, as big a giants now as they were in my days of the mighty Seventies. Also, they wear the crown of 'Sir' proudly and with dignity and respect, unlike some that are better not mentioned.

Britain has, over the decades, produced many world famous stars that could hold their own against any of the Hollywood greats.

But now we would struggle to find half a dozen that could fill their shoes.

Cast your eye on this list of mighty Hollywood legends alive and dead:

MALE
Rudolph Valintino
Errol Flynn
Clark Gable
Humphrey Bogart
John Wayne
Henry Fonda
Marlon Brando
James Stewart
Charlton Heston
Richard Burton
Paul Newman
Robert Redford
Woody Allen
Sidney Poiter
Sean Connery

Clint Eastwood
Richard Harris
Anthony Hopkins
Robert De Niro
Al Pacino
Michael Douglas
Kirk Douglas
Burt Lancaster
Cary Grant
James Cagney
Gary Cooper
Lee Marvin
Yul Brynner
Steve McQueen
Charles Bronson

FEMALE
Greta Garbo
Olivia de Haviland
Bette Davis
Joan Crawford
Vivien Leigh
Ingrid Bergman
Lauren Becall
Grace Kelly
Marilyn Munroe
Doris Day
Maureen O'Hara
Sophia Loren
Elizabeth Taylor
Audrey Hepburn
Jane Fonda

Goldie Hawn
Barbara Streisand
Shirley MacLaine
Raquel Welsh
Brigitte Bardot
Sally Field

Who can really compare today with this charismatic and talented might? Who is as photogenic, or has that screen presence?

These people came from a time where they were rightly labelled legends. With today's computer generated films that have no real acting presence, or with the reality tripe that is trawled out on our televisions, we will be hard pressed to find the next batch.

Talk shows now have to fucking big up third-raters and C list 'celebrities' because true class is so thin on the ground.

Sadly, when today's so-called chat show hosts get a true star on their shows they spend the whole time trying to take the piss out of them, and are not actually listening to a word they are saying. They are just waiting for their next intervention with a 'witty comment'. Tossers.

CHAPTER 10

Fit for What?

If a world force was invading the UK tomorrow, who would be up, primed, and ready to do their bit to save their birthright country?

Who would be up to show the patriotic bulldog fighting spirit that Winston Churchill spoke about during the dark days of World War II?

Well let's see. Half the inhabitants of the UK weren't born here, so don't really give a fuck, and would probably ship off home pretty rapidly. And another big percentage, that I refer to as 'the lost Brits', are mainly fat, bone idle, whingeing scroungers who have got a job on their hands to get their lard-asses off the sofa to collect their benefit cheque.

I don't exactly see an elite army of home guards lining up with a do-or-die attitude., ready to stand shoulder to shoulder to defend Queen and country.

Why?

Because we have gone soft.

England owns nothing these days and Britannia doesn't rule the fucking waves — and hasn't done for a long time. What has England got left these days if not its glorious past?

We sat back on our fat, overfed and overpaid backsides remembering about how Great Britain was, but in fact couldn't see it being snatched out from under our noses by every other nation under the sun.

Years back, we had a thriving industry. We had umpteen big British businesses and manufacturers working on our soil. Now we have nothing.

I read just this week that another iconic British brand has fallen into foreign hands. Branston Pickle was sold to Japanese firm Mizkan. I ask you, what are the Japanese going to do with fucking pickle?

Owner Premier Food also sold Branston Ketchup,relish, Salad Cream and Mayonnaise in a £92.5 million deal.

Branston was added to a long line of famous British brands sold abroad.

Others along the way are Sarson's Vinegar, Hayward's Pickles, Hartleys Jam. Cadbury's has even sold out to American giants Kraft. No wonder we haven't seen the Flake Girl for so long. I expect America will reinvent her as a sun bed tanned ladyboy. God help us!

Gone to the Yanks are our beloved Creme Egg, Flake, and Roses.

This is not new. Rowntree's, that was established in 1862, went to the Swiss in 1988. Smarties disappeared to the Germans in 2006, with the loss of 646 jobs in York. In 2008, Scottish & Newcastle, were sold to a consortium of Heineken and Carlsberg. So our British pint of John Smith's and Newcastle Brown Ale are owned by Dutch and Danish firms. Fucking hell.

Jaguar is owned by an Indian firm (it was previously owned by Ford.) So much for the classic British car. Wedgwood and Waterford Crystal are also owned by the US.

ICI, manufacturer of the famous Dulux paint, is now owned by the Dutch.

What about Heathrow airport operators BAA or P&O Ferries? Abbey National, or Scottish Power? all foreign owned.

Even the classic HP Sauce that proudly features the Houses of Parliament on its label moved to Holland.

Our Victorian ancestors paved the way for British industry. Coal, iron, copper, tin, porcelain, textiles, etc. etc. We had it all and threw it away. While we were busy fucking over some other country and stealing from them we lost sight of our own dear island which has gradually been taken off our hands by every other Tom, Dick and Harry.

Wasn't it Napoleon who called us a nation of shopkeepers? Not anymore. Most of the shopkeepers are the hardworking and business astute Asian community.

Why?

Because they work as a team, as a family. By doing this they can be open, if they want, for 24 hours a day.

Remember the days of the British cornershop owner? You would rush down at 5pm for a bottle of milk or a loaf of bread. He was shut. What about Sundays? Shut. No fucking chance.

The old-fashioned British shopkeeper hardly exists anymore. He got old, retired and his son/daughter thought, "Bollocks, I don't want to run that business." So what happened? He sold up shop was taken over by the Asian community, or it lay empty, dropping into a state of disrepair.

Who are the main grafters today in the UK? As mentioned before, the Asians and certainly, the Eastern Europeans. Hand car washes, what a brilliant idea. Did we think that up? No we fucking didn't. What a golden business opportunity that the Eastern European lads pounced on. Fair play to them. These guys will work any job for money and pride. They are doing the jobs that most Brits couldn't be assed to get out of bed for. They would rather have a handout from the social. If Hitler had his time again, we wouldn't be so lucky this time around.

We got fat, lazy, and complacent, and paid the price. The vast majority of the British now want it easy. They don't want to wait for anything or work for it. They want it handed to them on a fucking plate. In fact, they think it is their birthright.

When I was younger, you got your ass out to work as soon as you left school. No handouts given freely. A working attitude was instilled in me and a 'you get nothing for nothing in this world approach'. No easy rides.

I have no problem if the UK is multi-racial so long as they are working and putting something back into the country and willing to speak our language. Not coming over here for any easy life. Unfortunately, many are.

Some Brits moans about the fact foreigners are taking their jobs from them. There is some truth in that statement but there is also truth that we were too sluggish off the mark and missed the boat by being too slow, complacent and fucking lazy!

Recent statistics say that 1.5m Brits are morbidly obese. Last year 5,407 gastric band bypass operations were performed, compared to 858 back in 2006. Operations cost between £5,000 to £7,000, adding up to £50m a year from the NHS budget.

Diabetes and knee operations (both a by-product of being overweight) are up 53% in the last six years. 615,586 diabetics needed hospital treatment last year. 2.9m Brits have been diagnosed with diabetes and around 850,000 are undiagnosed.

Things are being made bigger to accommodate them, rather than the government and the health service making them lose weight.

No, we are fucking soft. So we are breeding a society that will have a job on their hands just to move. Instead, they will bleed the NHS dry looking for another pill, drug or operation.

We won't have to worry about too many cars on the road soon. We will be worrying about too many fucking mobility scooters.

You fat bastards out there, have some pride and lose some weight! You are responsible for yourselves!

Harsh? Okay, if there is a medical reason, that is different but for most it is an eating reason called gluttony! Nobody is force-feeding you food and you didn't become that size overnight. That takes some serious work.

Think of your body's skeleton as a clothes hanger. You put a coat on the hanger and it's okay. You put six coats, eight coats, ten coats etc. on it and it will bend, buckle or break. It is not designed to carry all that weight and neither is the human frame. It will give up just like the coat hanger.

Yes, the majority of knee and hip ops are down to obesity. Heart problems, high blood pressure, cholesterol problem, and yes, diabetes, are by-products of being a fat bastard.

I have many friends working in the health and fitness industry and the NHS. GP referral schemes in the gyms around the UK are jammed packed because of the obesity problem in this country.

Now, as a former gym instructor, I can have a certain amount of empathy with these people, but if they won't help themselves how can they expect somebody else to help them?

Airlines will penalise me for having a couple of extra kilos luggage and charge me whilst the two lard-asses sat next to me weigh 20 stone apiece.

I say that the airlines should charge by bodyweight — that will soon sort them out.

I am surprised that planes can get off the fucking ground seeing the majority of the people sat in them are grossly overweight.

Back in my day, the fat kid was singled out or bullied and you could count the number of fat kids on one hand. It was a novelty.

Now, some thirty years on, it's the other way round. Let's bully the skinny kid. They stand out amongst the sea of fatties. Amazing.

Who can we blame? Well, for a large part, the fast food franchises.

In the '70s, you had the Wimpy Burger Bar and you had to have a few quid in your pocket to eat there. That was it.

Now, for next to nothing, you can go into McDonald's, Burger King, Miss Millies, KFC, Subway, etc. Etc. and gorge yourself stupid.

Chips, pizzas, burgers, fried chicken. That's the staple diet of many.

Go into Wetherspoon's for a reasonably priced meal of lasagne or cottage pie (a meal on its own) and you have to have fucking chips with it. Chips with everything. Some people can't go a day without chips. In fact, some think it isn't a meal unless chips are on the plate.

Everywhere has gut-busting fry-ups. Crisps have to come in monster grab bags and chocolate bars have to come in mega-size or doubles. Everything the size of a brick.

Everything has got to be big so logically, if you buy into this diet so will your ass. It's not rocket science. We have inherited the American fast food eating habits.

Some say we are a nation addicted to alcohol. A reasonable argument in some circles but I say a bigger problem is addiction to Coca-Cola and fizzy drinks.

Everywhere you go, you see somebody frantically clinging to a bottle of Coke like their lives depended on it. Some are sat eating a fry-up and glugging down Coca-Cola at the same time. What's all that about?

The Action Men and Women of the '70s wouldn't have been seen dead doing this.

I was chatting to a friend of mine in the local council recently and he told me that he was reasonably informed that UK's kids are third in the world for being overweight, coming behind Chile and the USA. 25% are overweight. They spend thirty-five hours a week watching television. USA come in at 28% and they've got a shed load more channels and look at the size of the fucking place.

UK's kids spend eight hours a week playing video games. The USA spends seven and a half. Time spent online for UK's kids is fifty-one hours and ten hours spent texting. Only two-and-a-half hours are spent outside playing. It says it all, doesn't it?

When I was a kid, I was outside always playing, and all my mates and I managed to survive not being run over by a car, being sexually assaulted or being murdered.

What chance have the kids of today got when some obese celebrity is their role model? A world where we are mollycoddled to say that it's okay to be fat and we mustn't say anything about it. We shouldn't upset a person.

Yes, we should. If not, we are going to be a nation of blimps.

We won't have any sports stars or teams, no armies, no explorers. No heroes, because they won't be able to get out of the armchair. The only Guinness World Records we will be breaking is for who is the heaviest bastard in the country, or the person who ate one hundred pasties from Gregg's.

Ban the fucking school run and walk with your kids. Show them how to cross a road safely, talk about the dangers along the way. Give them one hour a day on a video game or computer.

Otherwise they will lose the ability to communicate in the real world and will flunk every job interview they get.

Get out with them and swim, kick a ball about, jog, whatever. But get your fucking arses off the sofa before it is too late. You only get one shot at life on this planet so do it right!

While we are on the subject of Gregg's, do you notice on a Saturday in the town or city centre, the longest queue for any shop is Gregg's? This bakery has become the centre of the universe for some. It is a major lifeline. The people that regularly inhabit it go into cold sweats if they don't get their fix of pastries, pies, pizza slices or cream cakes.

Britain has lost its identity. The American vision of all us Brits wearing bowler hats and suits, carrying a brolly, eating scones and jam and sipping mid-afternoon tea has long gone. It no longer exists.

I come from an era where you sat down with your family at the table for dinner, even if it was beans on toast.

You had a mum and dad who were married, and your brother or sister was your brother or sister.

When you went to school, you understood ninety percent of the names on the school register. It was safe to say 'blackboard'. You went on a cross-country run, no matter what your size, colour, or creed you were.

When you went swimming, whatever your religion, you got your swimming trunks or costume on and got in the fucking water. No questions asked.

You could fly the Union Jack or St. George's Cross proudly without upsetting somebody.

It was cool to put up Christmas decorations and a tree without hiding them away.

Policemen were six foot plus beasts who you didn't fuck with, and you saw them walking your neighbourhood regularly doing what they were supposed to do. Not sat behind a desk. Encountering a policeman these days is like finding a South American condor. A rare fucking breed indeed. If this state of affairs go on kids will be asking their parents, "What does a policeman look like, Mummy?"

Back in the day, we also had bin men who weren't frightened to handle a bin or go to the immense strain of picking up a few extra black bags.

Where you had respect for your neighbourhood clergyman, school master, and scout leader without thinking they were all paedophiles.

Teenagers did actually manage to string together a conversation rather than grunting a few words between playing on their computer and listening to their iPods, or texting on their phones.

Instead, you got off your ass and went down the road to make a phone call in one of those big red boxes called a phone box (remember them?) Then you'd walk half a mile to the next one because that one had been vandalised. No wonder we were fit.

A time when, if you were lucky enough to have a car, you didn't break your neck to park practically in a shop's doorway rather than parking up and walking a bit or using it to drive one hundred yards up the road to the newsagent.

This country now does not know who it is and it is not going to recover anytime soon.

Poor old Churchill would wonder what happened to the country he rallied to stop from being invaded.

Let's hope to God we don't come under threat again. The only possibility of resistance from the masses would be if the benefits office or Gregg's was going to be burned to the ground. Otherwise, we are fucked.

CHAPTER 11

A Quick Manly Lesson
in Self-Defence

Why does every man think that he can fight? Ask any average guy on the street and he feels that, when it comes down to it, he will know how to handle himself.

Well, the sad truth is the vast majority of males couldn't sleep-fight, beat an egg, or for that matter, batter fish.

They are deluded. Their fighting knowledge comes from watching fake fights on film.

They believe they are Bruce Lee, Chuck Norris, Steven Seagal, and Van Damme all rolled into one.

What is this stupid and näive attitude based on?

Now, I am not just talking about the ladyboy generation out there that we discussed at length in other chapters. Their biggest fight is opening their manbags, and whether they can drink their latté without burning their delicate lips.

No, I am talking about also 40 year old adolescents, muscle boys and schoolyard bullies. Also, beer bellied, tattooed, England football shirt wearing chavs, university rugby types and general gangster motherfuckers watching too much MTV.

The bottom line is ninety percent of men couldn't punch a hole in a fucking wet paper bag.

How do I know? Because my good friend Kevin and I have spent a lifetime around real fighters. Professionals that do it for a living and are fucking good at it.

These guys' every day work is based on how to give another human being as much pain as possible in as many different ways as they can.

They can punch with the power of a runaway train and the accuracy of a cruise missile. They can bend you into knots, choke you, break your limbs and mangle your internal organs so they resemble spaghetti.

They can put you to sleep faster than Ovaltine or a Coldplay record.

These people are the real fucking deal. They are in the minority. To see these guys in action is pure violent poetry. *A beautiful but deadly thing.*

But they have invested a lifetime to achieve this perfection.

The average person will not have the time, inclination, patience or fitness to achieve these high levels of skill.

So good old Clinton Steele with the help of my good pal Kevin, will outline here a condensed crash course in how to kick ass if you or your loved ones lives are threatened and you are in danger.

Time to fight like a real man and hit hard, fast and first.

I call my style of martial art Fuckthemupfastjutsu!

Fighting Myths

As I already stated most guys fighting knowledge is from the films. Hence, they are not real. They will do more harm than good.

Here are a few reality checks:

1. Being covered in tattoos, body piercings and pumping a bit of iron doesn't make you a fighter. No matter how much you posture, swagger and practice your thousand yard stare, it still won't cut it. Being a legend in your own mind is cruising for

a heavy fall. I know guys you would not give a second glance to with pipe thin arms, weighing nine stone, soaking wet that could tear you a new arsehole without raising a sweat. Looking the part doesn't mean you are the part. So, ditch the film star machismo and stop being a twat. Real men and real fighters don't walk around dragging their knuckles and snarling at everyone that crosses their paths, but bullies and arseholes do!

2. If you get smashed over the head with a blunt instrument you won't be up in five minutes running around like a two year-old. The fact is you will bleed a lot, and you'll probably be concussed. Possibly have a fractured skull, be unconscious or, at the very least, feel dizzy and nauseous. You will definitely not to be in the mood to fight.

If you are unconscious for a length of time, when you wake up you will have pissed yourself, maybe even shat yourself. You don't see that in the Bond movies!

3. If you get kicked in the nuts, you will lose the will to fight, and again you will not be up and recovered in a few minutes. If you are down from the nut-shot you will be in danger of being kicked to death.

4. Street fights are very fast and ferocious, a lot faster than you can imagine. There will be no sparring or dancing around like Muhammad Ali. Somebody will get up in your face and hit you without warning. If you are not switched on you will be out of the fucking fight before you know you are in it. Normally, the person who lands the first blow, unless he is totally useless, will win the encounter.

There is no block and parry shit, no ebb and flow, with a sprinkling of cheesy dialogue such as, "Is that your best shot, motherfucker." It is a three second assassination when done correctly.

5. You can't smash a beer bottle on the side of the bar and have a neatly jagged weapon at hand. Firstly, it takes a lot to break a bottle, and secondly, when it does break it smashes all over the place and will probably sever your hand. Movie bottles are made out of sugar glass.

6. You will not be executing complicated and fancy moves like Liam Neeson in '*Taken*.' The body will go into survival mode and you will be working on gross motor skills; e.g. one repetitive movement over and over until you win or lose, or get just plain exhausted.

7. Punching a person in the bony head means you will probably break bones in your hand, especially if you have been pushing pencils all your life. If you are not used to the exposure of full contact sparring, when you get hit it will fucking hurt, even with the adrenalin pumping in your blood stream.

8. Most people have forty-five seconds of fight in them and then they are fucked.

9. If you can't fight on the floor you are fucked.

10. If you can't land an accurate and hurtful blow in the first few seconds, you are fucked.

11. Most young guys on the street will either attack you as a group or use an edged weapon on you. If you have no training in either of these areas you are fucked.

SO... LISTEN UP...

Here is the first rule:

1. If you are about to be beat on by one or more individuals do not wait to be hit. If you can't escape, hit fast. Hit the biggest and ugliest one. Scream like a lunatic, look like a bloodcurdling killing machine, even if inside, you are shitting yourself. Play psycho. But inside, be in control.

2. If you want to bring a big bastard down to his knees, here are a few combat proven moves:

- Stomp with the sole of your boot into their kneecap – this will bring them down to size and crying like a baby.
- Smash your fist or knee up into their balls. Owwhh!
- Slap both your open palms over their ears for a concussive knockout.
- Ram the heel of your hand up viciously under their chin or nose – the heel of the hand is the preferred method of hitting the bony head, not your more fragile fist.
- If your life is on the line, attack the throat. Slash the edge of your hand (the classic Karate chop) into the windpipe or thrust the web of your thumb and forefinger into the throat.
- Smash the fleshy base of your fist down like a hammer onto the bridge of the nose.
- Spread your fingers like a claw and drive them into the eyes or grip the windpipe hard and squeeze and rip.
- Headbutt the nose with the dome of your forehead. The rule is headbutt with every part of your head above the eye line to everything below their eye line. The nose is the prime target.
- Elbows are like close range baseball bats: they can hit from all angles, and wherever you strike it will have an effect. Swing it across, back up, or down to do some serious damage.
- Swing your forearm like a bat into the side or back of an attacker's neck and they will hit the floor fast. When they are down on their knees a shot to the ribs or head will make sure they stay down! Brutal? Yes. But we are fighting for our lives here, not for a parking space in Asda.

If grappling:

- Seize the testicles and squeeze.

- Bite anything you can latch onto.
- Stick a thumb in an eye or drill it into the cavity behind the earlobe.
- You can thrust your fingers into the indentation at the base of the neck and the joint of the collarbones, or up the nostrils.
- Pull and twist the hair, moustache, or beard, etc.
- Hook a finger into the mouth, avoiding the teeth, and rip.
- Grab the head and pull it down into a rising knee to the face or into the body.

If grabbed in any shape or form from behind, use one or more of the following:

- Smash the rear of your head into their face.
- Stomp the insteps.
- Back elbow their body.
- Hammer fist or seize the groin.
- Reach up and find a little finger, and bend and snap it.

If you are on the floor with opponent standing over you:

- Kick out at their shins and knees until they back off and you can get up.
- Do not let your attacker get past your legs.
- If they do and they are kicking you, curl into a protective ball protecting your head. Look to grab their ankle and roll your body right through their knee, or latch onto their calf with your teeth and bite through it.

Against weapons your first option is to fucking run! If this is not an option, pick up an equaliser that you can use. Something big and scary, preferably.

Put a barrier in the way, a table, chair, dustbin, car, etc.

Use anything in sight, such as a stick, brick, brief case, laptop bag, shopping bag, umbrella, etc. as a weapon.

If you have no choice and you must fight barehanded, then attack the assailant. Run in and close them down, grab their weapon hand and beat the fuck out of them with your other free hand.

Remember, the body's weapons are the head, teeth, hands, elbows, knees, and feet. Don't forget your best weapon – your brain!

Once you have incapacitated the attacker, run! Don't wait and admire your handiwork.

Avoid violence and confrontation. Real men can talk then walk from a fight. Self-defence is different. Your only choice may be to defend yourself by fighting back.

If you believe your life or your loved ones are in jeopardy, fight back with a hundred percent commitment and ferocity. Give no quarter and no mercy.

Remember, it is not the size of the dog in the fight; it is the size of the fight in the dog. Also, don't be an asshole and pick fights and don't associate or go where assholes go. No matter how hard you think you are, there is someone out there harder.

If you choose to settle disagreements with your fists, you will go to jail. You won't pass 'Go' or pickup a £200. You will, however, be sharing a cell with an 18 stone, tattooed biker named Alice who will keep you company on dark, lonely nights. Also, it won't be Head & Shoulders shampoo you will be taking into the showers. It will be Alice!

Beware. Fighting is for playgrounds and mugs. Real men defend themselves only when all other options run out.

It takes a bigger man to walk away from a fight or have the verbal skills to talk your way out of a fight.

Our most powerful weapon is our brain. That's what separates us from the animal kingdom. That's what gives us an edge.

Put us naked up against any animal and we come a pretty poor second. We don't have claws, big fucking teeth, armour, scales, venom or stings. But we do have our brain. Use it to avoid violence, it is an unpleasant thing, but also know what to do when the shit hits the fan.

It is a man's responsibility to look after himself and his loved ones. Not cower behind a wall praying it will all go away.

Do not be a bully or abuse your fighting skills. I am a great believer in Karma and what goes around comes around. Conduct yourself like a gentleman and shit will normally bypass you. But don't be naive. Trouble can rear its ugly head anywhere, simply because there are a lot of arseholes around.

Most want to posture and bad mouth you. They are bullies and probably won't step over the line if you don't play their stupid games. But some are predators. They are sociopaths that cannot be reasoned with. They are a rare breed but if you come across one and you can't escape you will be fighting for your life. So get some training in beyond a fighting game on the Xbox.

Real men also teach their ladies, children and loved ones how to defend themselves, and if they can't they will be man enough to send them to somebody who can show them. Mrs Steele and I spend many a happy hour rolling around getting sweaty and dirty on the floor. I recommend it. But that's another story!

To lighten the mood of this chapter here is a joke for you.

Why doesn't Mike Tyson like Playstations?

Because he is an ex-boxer!

The Dirty Dozen

Twelve techniques to stop the street predator in their tracks and make them regret the day they fucking targeted you as a victim!

1.   Knee stomp, arc hand to throat, and spike kick to balls.
2.   Knee stomp, knee to solar plexus, downward elbow/hammer fists to base of skull.
3.   Double ear slap, arc hand throat, palm heel nose, stomp kick knee.
4.   Double ear slap, grab ears head butt nose, shoulder slam into nose, knee balls, bite the face, head twist to floor, slam head into ground.
5.   Back hand slap to balls, double ear slap. Elbows to head
6.   Reverse knife hand to throat, palm heel chin, and knee the balls.
7.   Eye rake, uppercut to balls, downward elbows to base of skull.
8.   Lead arc hand jab to throat, fore-knuckle strike to throat, push/twist shoulder into rear naked choke
9.   As above, into rear naked strangle.
10.   Attacker at your side: vertical elbow to chin, reverse knife hand throat, palm heel chin, knee balls.
11.   Attacker from side: reverse knife hand to neck, dropping uppercut to balls, head/chin twist, downward head butt to temple.
12.   Attacker standing at rear of you: downward groin slap, vertical elbow to chin, reverse knife hand to throat, side kick stomp to knee.

Over and fucking out.

Main vulnerable points to strike on the male body:

- Throat/neck
- Eyes
- Jaw/chin
- Base of skull/nape of neck
- Temples
- Ears
- Groin
- Knees/shins
- Spine

CHAPTER 12

Manly Things to Do Before you Die

There are certain things that a male has to do to prove his manliness before he dies. Reading this, you should already be thinking, "Yep, done that, and that, and that." Or maybe just saying, "Yep, I am going to do that."

If you aren't, then you do not deserve the honour of being male, and probably need to book in for a sex change operation right now.

Right, check out the following and start ticking them off!

• **Be in charge of a barbeque.** This is a privilege and an honour for any man. Grilling raw meat wearing nothing but a pair of shorts is totally manly. Even if it is raining, don't give a fuck. Get grilling! Women love to see a man take control of a barbeque. Also, cooking a big fry up in just your boxers is up there too. Don't flinch if the cooking oil spits and splashes. You are hard. You can take it.

• **Play a contact sport and pursue a dangerous past time.** Real men play a contact sport or like to pursue a crazy pastime. It bonds men firmly as brothers when they participate in a tough, challenging and potentially life threatening pastime. Be a cage fighter, rugby player, boxer, surfer, iron man challenger, bungee jumper, rock climber, hang glider etc. You get the picture. Do something that triggers the fear factor and gets the adrenaline pumping. Not badminton or golf!

- **Cutting down a tree and chopping logs**. Both worthy things to do. Wanton destruction of a tree is manly. Swinging a big fucking axe is great. You wouldn't fuck with a lumberjack, would you? So get fucking chopping.

- **Lighting fireworks**. Men love to see things explode. If we could throw sticks of dynamite and hand grenades around all day we would. A firework is the next best thing. Always light them with confidence and swagger. Don't flinch like a pussy. Also, be big and approach a fizzled out firework and light it again.

- **DIY**. Now, don't become a DIY bore, spending your weekends in B&Q, but if you need to get out a monster drill or hammer and do a job, get on with it and do it.

- **Catch a big fucking fish**. If you are going to fish, get out somewhere and catch a big vicious bastard just like Jeremy 'there is no fish alive that I can't catch' Wade of *River Monsters* fame. Wade is a proper fucking man. He isn't sat in the local park fishing in the lake for a tadpole. He is out their catching fucking great white sharks and its like. Think of Quint in the film *Jaws*;

- **Sharpen a knife**. This is a manly thing to do. Do it sat by a camp fire, and then open up a tin of peaches with it and eat them off the end of the knife. Yes, this is pure man.

- **Wrestle a bear or a crocodile.** Yes, anything wild and dangerous, get down on the deck and wrestle it. Think of Tarzan. He wrestled lions, sharks, crocodiles and all sorts of dangerous shit. Rolling around with your pet poodle doesn't count.

- **Throw a punch and learn to take one.** Reference the previous chapter for all sorts of bad shit you can do to somebody who wants to fuck you up.

- **Change a car tyre.** Every man, once in their lives, will have to do it. Learn how to do it well without having to call out the emergency breakdown. They will do it for you, but inwardly think you are a poof!

- **Have a threesome.** You know you want to. Don't deny it. It is an extremely manly thing to do.

- **Eat crazily spicy and hot things.** To be a real man you have to do pickles, peppers, sauces, curries, chillies... whatever. As long as it makes your eyes water, takes your sense of taste completely away for a week, and has you shitting through the eye of a needle.

- **Learn to play an electric guitar.** Ever wonder why butt-ugly rock stars get all the gorgeous chicks? You got it; they can play an electric guitar like an extension of their penis. It is an instantly manly way of turning on the ladies.

- **Learn CPR.** Everyone, not just men, should have these basic first aid life saving skills. Get on a course now if you haven't got CPR skills.

- **Make a fire.** Men love messing around with fire. Our early ancestors discovered it, and it helped them survive harsh weather and helped cook their food. There is something highly satisfying and manly about making a big roaring fire.

- **Learn to swim.** The world is around seventy percent water so you are bound to be in it sometime. So be able to survive. Remember the Titanic!

- **Eat a big steak.** Yes, men seek out a fucking big steak and consume it in one sitting. There are plenty of restaurants that offer this challenge. Find one and do it now. Remember, real men eat meat.

- **Read a map.** Men don't like to ask for directions or trust SatNavs. Learn how to map read and find your way to or from anywhere. Men should have at least one map in their car.

- **Ride a motorbike.** Bikes are cool and sexy. There is something macho about riding a motorbike. Remember Dennis Hopper and Peter Fonda in the film '*Easy Rider.*' Class.

- **Carry heavy things.** It is manly to hump big heavy things around. Even if you have got help, lift it yourself and bust your balls doing it.

- **Learn to clean and shoot a gun.** It makes sense (only if it's legal!)

- **Get totally hammered.** Not just drunk but bladdered so you lose a day or so. It just makes sense to do, even if it is just once.

- **Never hit women.** No, it's not manly in any shape or form. It is a despicable and cowardly thing to do (play fighting is fun and okay to do, so is a little smacking if it is part of an enjoyable sexual game.)

- **Know how to protect your family.** Reference the chapter on fighting, etc.

- **Cook a signature dish.** Real men don't fanny around in the kitchen too much, but have one thing you can cook well to impress the ladies.

- **Do something gentlemanly or romantic.** Yes, you don't have to be a complete knuckle-dragger. Treat a woman right and have a little respect. Try and remember birthdays, anniversaries and Valentine's Day.

- **Type with more than two fingers.** In this day and age of computers, expand those keyboard skills.

- **Stand up and make a speech.** Have the ability and balls to stand up in public if warranted and make a speech. Be confident and clear. Real men feel the fear and do it anyway.

- **Have the ability to capture a room's attention.** Have the charisma and charm to captivate a room when you walk into it, and the intellect to keep an audience enthralled in your stories and anecdotes. Don't be a boring asshole and know when to shut the fuck up.

- **Find talking about breaking wind and shit highly amusing.** Along with sex, this subject can keep a man amused for hours.

- **Hug another man.** Be confident enough in your sexuality to hug another man under the right circumstances. Learn to do it for the appropriate length of time and, under no circumstances, breathe in his ear or let your hand drift to his buttocks.

- **Grow food.** If we had a zombie invasion, you would love to have the knowledge of how to grow something to eat in order to survive. Start learning those skills now.

- **Learn to take harsh criticism.** Real men can take it on the chin without sulking or bitching. If it is constructive criticism then embrace it, learn from it and move on.

- **Grow a beard.** Definitely a manly thing to do. If you are going to do it make sure it is proper and not some wispy girly thing that the cat could lick off.

- **Drink, fight, fart, fuck and laugh.** That's what real men do. We are hard wired for it and we can't be changed, ladies.

The list can go on and on but you should have the message by now. If you can't relate to all or any, of these things you seriously have a problem. To help you out, the next chapter will give you a list of unmanly things to avoid like the plague.

CHAPTER 13

Unmanly Things to Not Do
Before you Die

Listed below are the things a real man shouldn't do under any circumstance, no matter what your wife or girlfriend may tell you. In this modern day of the confused male you need to sort yourself out and know your place in this world. Read and heed:

- **Wear hair wax or gel** -A big girly and gay thing to do.

- **Wax your body** – We have discussed this at length elsewhere in this book, so don't do it.

- **Go to a boy band concert** – That is a death sentence for a real man. Also, don't own any of their CDs either.

- **Go to an aerobics class** – Now go and find manly exercises and ditch the leotard and leg warmers.

- **Eat salad** – Unless it is accompanied by a fucking big steak or chicken breast.

- **Wash dishes** – Can you see Chuck Norris stood at a sink with a pair of Marigold gloves on? No, you can't. Get a dishwasher or your wife. (Isn't this the same thing?)

- **Whistle or singing a Cheryl Cole song** – This is not on. We are not just talking Cheryl. Any girly song in the charts.

- **'Does my ass look big in these?'** – You are a man. Forget it. Who fucking cares?

- **Sing in the shower** – Just don't. It's not right for a man to do this.

- **Use fruity lotions** – A real man doesn't smell of peach, coconut, or mango. So don't use these female products.
- **Buy any female beauty products** – This goes with the above statement. You are a man. Buy men things.
- **Shave more than twice a week** – Your face doesn't have to be as smooth as a baby's bum all the time. Women like a bit of stubble. It tickles them, especially between the thighs!
- **Watch soap operas** -You must have better things to do than watching an hour of doom, gloom, and shite. Get real.
- **Use a tanning bed** -You don't need to walk around like a fucking tangerine. Let the sun naturally do it.
- **Own a poodle** – This goes for any other little girly dog. You will look a right prat walking it down the road.
- **Eat chocolate and worrying about putting on weight**
- **Watch** *The Only Way is Essex* – No, life is too short.
- **Ask for directions** – Men just don't do it.
- **Drink pear cider, or anything with a cherry in it** – It's gay. Could you imagine Clint Eastwood walking into a saloon, or Jack Regan stepping into a West London boozer and asking for a bottle of Smirnoff Black Ice? They would have been shot on the spot.
- **Have a tongue ring** – Asshole.
- **Drive a girly car-** e.g. Mazda Miata, Volkswagen Beetle, Nissan Micra, BMW convertibles. You get the idea.
- **Go to Starbucks and ordering a drink that isn't just an Americano-** That is what men drink. Simple. Anything else, apart from normal tea, is for wimps.
- **Get sex advice from a gay man** – Why would you?
- **Wear Speedos, bikini briefs or mega short shorts** – All banned and a major turn off.

- **Carry your lady's handbag** – Do that and you are on the path to ruin and female domination.
- **Shop more often than your lady** – Same reason as above.
- **Comment, "I think they are lovely"** when a female asks, "What do you think of my new shoes."
- **Guess a women's age when she says** "How old do you think I am?"
- **Never watch a women weigh herself and say** "Bloody hell, you've piled it on a bit!"
- **Go to a restaurant and eat** big girly dessert like a chocolate fudge brownie or Death By Chocolate.
- **Have shirtless images of yourself on Facebook** when loads of males are logging on.
- **Look at yourself constantly in a mirror** – You know who you are. Get on with it!
- **Talking to another male in a sport centre changing room when** you or him are bollock naked. Even worse if you both are. Shades of '*Top Gun*' coming on...
- **Have your lady ring up your workplace to tell them you are feeling poorly** – Big wimp.
- **Change your clothes more than once before you leave the house** – Keep it real. Clean and tidy.
- **Watch cooking and home improvement programmes** – Dodgy territory for a real man.
- **Enjoy house cleaning and hoovering** – Same reasons as above.
- **Wear open-toed sandals and socks** – Fashion suicide.
- **Be drunk after two pints** – Totally unacceptable.
- **Giggle and shouting "Oh my God!"** – You are not Janice from *Friends*
- **Remember your mate's birthday** – Blokes just don't.

- **Complain that any food is too spicy** – There is no such thing.
- **Unable to kick a ball** – You don't have to be Ronaldo, but if you need to kick a ball back to someone, don't end up looking like Bambi.
- **Unable to lift your own bodyweight** – Every real man should be able to aspire to lift at least lift his own bodyweight in the gym in some shape or form.
- **Unable to drive** – All men drive. Learn.
- **Sitting down to pee.**
- **Scream like a wimp on a rollercoaster** -Man up.
- **Unable to drink Jack Daniel's straight** –"Jack Daniel's" is the ultimate man drink. A splash of Coke is acceptable with it if you are a boy.
- **Grass a man out to a women** – Not good.
- **Bitch, moan and have hissy fits** – Real men suck it up and get on with things.
- **Bake a fucking cake or sponge.**

This is not an exhaustive list but it will get you started on the road to manliness.

CHAPTER 14

The Steele soapbox

I have, throughout this book, given a candid and no holds barred account of what I see wrong with the male of today. But there are many more issues that piss me off on a regular basis.

So I thought in this closing chapter I would let off a little more steam and unload some of my pet-hates. The ones I am about to talk about are, by no means, the complete list but they are my major gripes. I am a man of the '70s. I don't shun the modern society and its progress, but sometimes I long for the simpler days.

Yes, some might say I am a grumpy old bastard but I say I have been on this planet more than half a century and have earned the right to have a fucking moan. So let's begin...

Mobile phones

What really pisses me off is people driving and talking on a mobile phone. It is totally and utterly against the law. But they completely ignore this fact. Now, if it is against the law, then it's about time the boys in blue started reinforcing it.

It is the biggest crime being committed day- in day-out, and it is going unpunished. Time for the police to pull their finger out and start doing their job. If a law was passed in court and deemed viable, then why the fuck does nobody adhere to it!

If it is seen as dangerous driving then it has got to be up there with driving without a seatbelt, or drunk driving, surely? I read a while ago about two people cautioned by the police for eating as they drove. A banana and a KitKat were the offending sources of food. If this is justified, then what about mobiles?

If you are not going to reinforce this law then scrap it, because it is severely fucking me off.

Another aspect of mobiles phones is that they were a great invention for that emergency call, particularly for children if they needed help or were in a fix. Also, brilliant for the lone female if, for example, her car broke down and she needed to phone for help without exposing herself to danger.

To me, that is what the mobile offers: the comfort of knowing you are a phone call away from help. But, for most people now, it seems that making a call on a mobile is the last fucking thing they want to do. If the phone doesn't make your bed and dinner for you, and guide around a space satellite at a touch of a button and a million other totally non-essential things it's deemed crap and must be traded in instantly.

Use it to call somebody for something important. Forget the other crap.

I was a guy who came from a time where my parents finally got a phone put in their house. I could have cried for joy. No more ringing my girlfriend up in a metal box with broken windows and the wind whistling around your ass. The phone box's interior always smelling of piss and beer and having to kick around used chip wrappers and coke cans to find standing room so you could search your pocket for a handful of ten pence pieces.

To have that indoor phone was a bloody luxury, and I didn't give a fuck that it couldn't take a photo or play the latest chart sounds.

Don't you also think, men — MEN are you out there — that the mobile has been used as a tool for the female of the species to check on your every waking movement? You know it's true, but you're out hiding behind your gay side again, aren't you? Man up and tell her that unless it is a life and death emergency do not phone me for an idle chit-chat, or ask me what I am doing or where I am.

Remember men, when the phone rings and you see your beloved's name on the screen you do not have to immediately drop everything and answer it.

If you are at work, in the gym, or in the pub, that is where you are until otherwise. If you have told her this on the way out then she knows where you are and doesn't need to interrupt you unless it is serious. Sort it, lads!

If you don't then where is today's male sanctuary? You can be contacted even when you are having a piss. Is nothing sacred? A real man needs real man time to himself, and ladies, you have to respect and accept this fact.

When I went to work at an 8-to-5 job, you never got a phone call. If you did you would panic, as you guessed it was bad news. Something may be wrong with your family. Your wife didn't ring you up to tell you what a shit day she was having. It just wasn't done. If anybody's wife did habitually phone work, their spouse was threatened with the sack. This is no lie. Or his work mates would take the piss out of him for being under the thumb.

The male sanctums of the workplace: pub, club, garden shed, allotment, etc. have been allowed to be invaded by women due to fucking mobiles. This is not on, men. Put a stop to it now. Otherwise, picture the scenario: your phone goes and you answer it. Your spouse asks, "What are you up to, babe?" You reply, "I am sat on the bog at work having a crap. Is that okay, or should I go into more detail?"

Don't you think mobile devices have made people rude? There is no conversation any more. Everybody is fiddling with phones, iPads and DS's. You sit in Costa or Starbucks and every bastard is on some sort of electronic device, while some other poor sod is sat their stirring their coffee for the thousandth time, waiting for the other one to come off the fucking thing.

I read recently that one shop is making a stand not to serve a person at the counter if they are jabbering or texting into their phone and not acknowledging the person serving them. Good bloody show. It is fucking unacceptable, and worth a good kick in the liver.

People bumping into you in the street while texting or on the phone is a fucking nuisance as well. Talking into a hands-free kit as you walk along makes you look like a fucking crazy person. Worse still is when you are sat on a bus and they're loudly talking a load of bollocks.

People can't hold a conversation face-to-face for two minutes without reaching for that phone. Learn some manners and put it away unless it is some dire emergency. Let's become human again.

While we are at it, if I am talking to you, take the fucking earphones out as well. Otherwise you won't have any ears to hang them from!

Police

Don't get me wrong, I am not anti-police. We need to uphold the law of the land. But the aforementioned mobile phone crimes happen mainly because people think it is worth the gamble. Let's face it. What is the chance of a police car, police bike, policeman on foot, etc. tapping on your car window and catching you?

Answer – probably nil! Because they are chained to a desk bogged down in paperwork, red tape and bureaucratic bullshit.

If you ask most individuals who joined the police force why they did, sitting on their asses behind a desk for eight hours a day probably wouldn't be their answer.

Government, wake up and don't let our police turn into soft, lazy, pencil pushing desk jockeys. Get police out onto the streets. Let their presences be seen and felt and I guarantee crime will drop.

People are up to all sorts of no-good on our streets because they know the police are nowhere to be seen and when they are their hands are tied with red tape and such bollocks.

Now, if some poor sod is getting mugged or terrorised by some feral little fucker the police will not be seen for hours.

But give them a football match, open air concert, carnival or protest march, and you are tripping over the bastards. Amazing, isn't it?

When I was a kid, police were always on the street walking! Yes, read that again, WALKING. They were known in your neighbourhood and proud to walk their patch, and keep crime at bay.

If you were up to no good and a policeman caught you, he would give you a clip around the ear and frog-march you to your parents. Job done. But now the parents are as bad as their shitty offspring so it doesn't work!

I say grab them, put them in a black transit van, take them somewhere quiet, and beat the shit out of them; then dump them back in their neighbourhood with the promise of more to come if they fuck up again. That will sort it.

Have an elite team of coppers. Big hairy-ass fuckers built like brick shit-houses. Train them to be monsters and then give them the authority, when warranted, to get out on the streets and punch, kick, baton, CS gas and generally fuck some little shit up if they are stepping out of line.

We should take a leaf from some other countries' books and have a zero tolerance policy. Do I hear an outcry? Only if you are a fucking criminal.

Pricks in the gym

I have trained all my life, near as damn it, in gyms, and no matter which one I've trained or worked at you always find a prick. In fact, usually more than one.

These guys really do piss me off big time. You see, there is more than one type of prick in the gym, or would they come under the category of asshole instead? Now, that's a tough one. Anyway, here are a few of the most common:

A) The Hard Man – This species believes in his pea-like brain that humping some weight around and getting a bit of a build somehow makes him a tough guy. You know the type. Strutting around, arms splayed, chest puffed out in a tiny micro-vest. He walks like he has just shat himself and hasn't quite finished yet. The hard stare, the glare, the snarl, likes to grunt a lot, and drop weights with a loud crash.

Now, I know guys who lift a lot of weight and are tough. But the majority aren't. They are hiding behind their muscle-plated armour, hoping no-one ever steps up for a look beyond the cosmetic steroid-pumped physique.

Lifting weights does not make you a fighter. Real fighters train to fight. Weights are a small part of their regime. Also, don't mistake 'big' for 'hard'. Never judge a book by its cover and never presume that because you are bigger, or have a better build then some other guy that you are somehow superior. Many have made that mistake in the past and paid a heavy price.

B) Bicep curler – This guy spends hours sat on a bench curling a dumbbell while checking himself out in the mirror. He believes big arms are the key to a great physique. He is a misguided soul, wasting his time and energy. Day-in day-out he is doing the same thing and getting nowhere fast. His big arms come from mindless hours in the gym and lonely nights on his own. I mean, how can there be women in his life when he spends more time in front of a mirror than her!?

My advice is: don't sit on anything in a gym. Gym machines like a chest press, shoulder press, etc. were designed for victims of traumatic accidents that ended up with a psychological or physical impairment. Now they have become the lazy trainer's staple diet.

We, as human beings, are dynamic machines built for movement, not sitting down. If you sit at a desk all day for work, why come into a gym afterwards and sit?

If you want to lift weights properly and get great results do deadlifts, squats, clean and press, chin-ups, pull-ups, tricep dips, one arm rows, military presses and their like.

Barbells and dumbbells, also kettle bells. Swing them, snatch them, rotate them, and pull them. Be progressive, dynamic, and move.

Get off your ass! Three sets of properly long arm chin-ups will give your biceps all the work they need!

C) The Fat Boy – This lad poses around in a vest top and presumes he has a great build. He likes to refer to himself as big, but in fact, he is fat.

He carries too high a percentage of puppy body fat and if he trained hard, worked up a sweat, and lifted properly, he would drop weight and body fat, and look ripped and a whole lot better. But it probably won't happen. He is too far up his own ass.

He usually also has a bunch of weasely, skinny little mates with him that look up to him as if he was Schwarzenegger himself. Fucking losers.

Usually this person is a university rugby type. Big fish in a little pond. Likes to wear a weightlifting belt when he is squatting forty kilos. Unfortunately, he won't listen to sound advice. He knows it all and will remain fat.

D) Over Forties Bench Presser – This final species has come back to the gym after a twenty year layoff, but in his mind he still thinks he's a young man. He has developed a beer gut and his tattoos are fading, but he struts around like a cockerel and stills believes he is 'The Boy.'

Instead of beasting out some cardio to lose weight and burn fat so he doesn't have a heart attack, he spends the gym session laid under the Smiths machine bench pressing. When he stands up he self consciously sucks his flabby belly in and pulls back his rounded shoulders, believing he is still defying Father Time.

On this note, a bench press has always seemed to be the benchmark for strength. If this is the case, why isn't it in Olympic weightlifting?

These are the main gym pricks. While we are on the subject, let's recap; unless you are physically or psychologically impaired, or over 50, don't sit on machines.

Also, unless you are the above mentioned don't sit on a bike peddling and reading a book. That is a total waste of time. If I read a book while peddling a bike, it would be turned into soggy pulp within thirty minutes.

Cut out posing in the mirror like a 'mince', cut out talking bullshit, letching after the females and scratching your balls and you can be more productive in less time.

Extremists, suspected terrorists, illegal aliens and fucking wasters

If you don't like our country, its policies, laws and rules, then the solution is easy... fuck off back to your own!

I don't care what colour, creed or religion you are, if you are spouting on about how shit the UK is and how the Western people are the devil reincarnated then fuck off!

We have become soft and let every wasting fucker into our country. They have infiltrated it, milked the system and then abused it. What do the government do? Nothing.

It wouldn't happen in the States or Australia for instance.

Imagine being out on their streets bad mouthing their country or burning their flag. You would be shot down like a dog, and quite rightly.

Or imagine going to a Middle Eastern country and standing in the streets, preaching about the Roman Catholic faith and bad mouthing Islam. How long would you last before you were chopped into pieces by a crazy mob? Not fucking long.

Here, though, we endure it all and the person born and bred in the UK feels like a second class citizen. It is he whom is discriminated against in his own country. He, who has worked all his life, paid National Insurance and taxes all his life and he is treated like shit.

He wouldn't be allowed to claim for as much as a postage stamp. Yet, others can come to this country, never work, never contribute, slag it off and claim thousands. *Fucking incredible.*

Paedophiles

Execute the fuckers. Don't lock them up. Chop off their balls and then do them in. Better still, lock them in a room with the child's relatives and let them see to it. Same goes for rapists and serial killers. Don't clog up the prisons and waste tax payers money. These scum are beyond help. Do the bastards in today. Problem solved.

People that don't return your phone calls or e-mails

These people are the scourge of the earth. I hate it when somebody says that they'll phone you back, or they'll get back to you, and they don't. Then you have to phone them again.

It is a shit way of working and shows total incompetence. How these people run a business is beyond me when they work this way.

Also, how some people get and hold down, a job of some importance is a fucking mystery.

Most people I deal with in the public sector are a waste of space. A trained chimp could do a better job.

If you are paid to manage, make decisions, and be a boss, then fucking do it, you spineless bastard. You get the salary, now fucking earn it and treat people properly!

What about automated phone calls? You have to go through twenty button presses to talk to a human being, then when you get there they can't understand you, and you can't understand them. Fucking marvellous. This is all called progress. Good God. Bring back the simple life of the Seventies.

Junk e-mail

This one is short and sweet. Stop sending me e-mails on penis enlargement. This is Clinton Steele you are talking too. A man who can give furniture a multiple orgasm by just sitting on it. A man whose penis is so large it still has snow on it in summer time. A man so good in bed that he screams out his own name. No lady has ever woken up in the morning and made Clinton his breakfast, washed up, and ironed his shirt without being totally satisfied. Amen.

Overpaid footballers.

Whether a modern day footballer is paid too much is one debate. If a club allows his agent to negotiate an obscene salary, who is he to turn it down. I'm sure I wouldn't, and probably not you either. What I do detest is the whingeing headlines of some footballers in the newspaper such as 'MY HELL'. What Hell is that? The Hell where you have got to sit on the subs bench, or the one where you got caught shagging a young strumpet? Oh yes, it must be terrible, you soft bastard. Hell is being the victim of a natural disaster, a rape, abuse, being a prisoner of war!

Today's footballer is a pampered poodle that hasn't got to lift a finger to survive. He doesn't live in the real world. Their arrogance and totally bigheaded self-belief that they are something special is beyond comprehension. They kick a ball around for God's sake. They are not brain surgeons.

I remember the days when a Sunday roast was a roast beef meal around the table with your family, not passing a young woman around a hotel bedroom.

The word 'world class' is bandied around all too freely. If you haven't been part of a World Cup winning squad, or at least got to the final, then you are not world class.

They should realise that they are in a privileged position and act accordingly. They would also do well to remember that it is the average Joe Public that pay his wages. They should make sure the gap between them and the fan doesn't get any bigger. Dumping the self pitying headlines is a good place to start.

While we are on this subject, read this list of footballers from the Seventies and Eighties. These guys were the real deal. They were hard as nails. You wouldn't see them taking a dive or faking injury. They would have played on with their head hanging off. These men did not have the luxuries of today's golden boys, but they loved a game and a good kick at someone. This was when football was tough.

- Dave MacKay
- Graham Souness
- Ron 'Chopper' Harris
- Tommy Smith
- Norman Hunter
- Billy Bremner
- Joe Jordan
- Billy Bonds
- Jimmy Case
- Terry Hurlock
- Neil 'Razor' Ruddock
- Peter Storey
- Vinnie Jones
- Stuart Pearce

No pretty boys here. Just real men. Their pre-match preparation was a stick of Wrigley's spearmint gum and a rub of Deep Heat on the legs. No preening and posturing in the mirrors. No exotic haircuts, no hair gel, no hair bands, no long sleeve undershirts and no fucking tights or gloves.

Imagine in the Seventies players wearing any of that shit. They would have been slaughtered on the pitch by the other players and the crowd. Plus they wouldn't have been welcomed in the communal bath. Poor old Brian Clough would be turning in his grave if he saw this now. No doubt so would other football managerial legends such as Bill Shankly or Sir Matt Busby.

Fashion was way down on the list of priorities then for a footballer. If he had his own two front teeth he was fucking happy.

The few pretty boy players of the era, such as George Best, Stan Bowles, Peter Maronelli, and Alan Hudson had to be bloody good runners and ball players to survive the brutal tackling of the game then.

There was no tripping over imaginary tackles, or falling down like you were shot in the back looking for a penalty. If you tried that shit you would get another kick. When you went down in a match in the Seventies you went down for real, especially if Ron 'Chopper' Harris nailed you.

The game had no room for whingers or fakers.

To finish on this passionate rant, I recall the story of Leicester city's playboy forward Frank Worthington, a fantastic player:

In a match against Liverpool he went past legendary Scouse hard man Tommy Smith like he wasn't there. Later, when Smith caught up with Worthington in the penalty box he growled in his ear, 'Do that again and I will break your fucking back". Worthington drifted out of the game after this remark.

JOKE TIME

Roy Hodgson said to Wayne Rooney just before the half-time break in the latest England match, "You are going to have to wake up here lad, or I will have to pull you off at half-time." Veteran coach Gary Neville, sat on the bench next to him, said, "Bloody hell. Back in my day, all we got was half an orange and a cup of tea!"

Men's fashion

I like to buy my own clothes. I pride myself on the fact that I can still look good at my age when most middle aged men look like they are fifteen months pregnant, and have more chins than a Chinese phone book.

But I am finding it increasingly more difficult to get a shop that will cater for me. I am not, and hopefully never will be, ready for the Marks and Spencer's cream slacks and cardigan range. But have you wandered around H&M, Topman, or Burton lately? What the fuck is happening? Does today's male really wear the shit they have on display.

What are all this gaily coloured t-shirts and trousers about? Lime green, lilac, pink, pastel, pouse, violet, lemon... All of them scream girl, girl, girl! Why would any self-respecting male want to wear these colours? How manly can you feel walking next to your lady?

But this is not the worst things that are happening in the world of male fashion. There are now men's Ugg boots called 'Muggs'.

That is total fucking horror, but I can top this. Asda do a range of underwear for the modern male called 'body sculpt trunks'. They are body shaping pants made from a material called Manx. These garments are designed so you don't show your pants line through your trousers! Oh sweet angel of death, take me now. The world is falling apart...

There are numerous men's fashion websites discussing the merits of summer knitwear, and how to wear your shorts for best effect. Imagine your Dad back in the day, down the local pub chewing the fat about the best sandals to wear on holiday! I think not.

Battle of the sexes

I do love the ladies but they do not come from the same planet as men do they lads? LADS! Don't be afraid to agree now, we have got this far into the book.

Here is a list of thing women just can't do...

- Anything about a car except its colour.
- Understand a movie plot.
- Read a map.
- Throw or catch a ball.
- Park.
- Fart.
- Understand the offside rule.
- Get told off without crying.
- Walk past a shoe shop.
- Argue without shouting.
- Go more than two minutes without sending a text message.
- Bitch about other women.
- Use small amounts of toilet paper.
- Stop themselves from hogging all the duvet.
- Drink a pint gracefully.
- Set a DVD recorder.
- Get to the point.
- Take less than half an hour in the bathroom.
- Get a round in.
- Throw a punch.
- Buy a purse that fits in their pocket.
- Decide to buy the first item of clothes they try on, rather than return four hours later to buy it.
- Eat a kebab whilst walking.
- Play pool.

- Pee out of a train window.
- Eat just one chocolate out of a box.
- Not have a dessert when they go out for a meal.
- Let you have sex when you want it.

Here are a few little jokes at our ladies expense:

Q: -What food reduces a women's sex drive by ninety percent?

A: -Wedding cake!

Q: -What is the difference between a woman and a mobile phone?

A: -You can put the phone on silent!

Q: -What's long and hard, and makes women moan?

A: -An ironing board!

Oh ladies, I hear you screaming and cursing, but you know it's true. I'm sure you can think of a lot of things men can't do, but hey, this is my book and it's about resurrecting the real male. A man ready to fight his corner and speak his mind, not one that will give in to your every argument and then put your relaxation tape of dolphins on the CD player and bring you your favourite ice cream.

Cyclists

Now I tread on dodgy territory here, as many members of my family ride bikes. But it has to be said that many cyclists work on double standards. I know there are some brain dead motorists out there who seem to gain pleasure out of fucking up people on bikes, and can be damn right dangerous by driving too close to cyclists or opening their doors without looking. Yes, these people are assholes and many bikers have the right to shout that motorists do not heed them, and that they are seen as second class citizens and nuisances on the roads.

Some do have a case, and just when I might be leaning towards their arguments I encounter, on a daily basis, some prick on a bike riding up the road the wrong way on the wrong side. Or better yet, blatantly riding through red lights when cars are stopped at them. Driving up on the pavements in front of old ladies or mums with prams and basically ignoring every rule of the Highway Code as if it doesn't apply to them.

Since when is it okay for a cyclist to please themselves on our roads? They have to abide by the rules, the same as the motorist, whether we like it or not. I don't relish waiting at a set of temporary traffic lights, but that's life. I don't just steam on through them.

My problem is that any brain dead bastard can buy a bike and be unleashed on our roads without any clue or regard for our Highway Code. That is fucking worrying. I know there are good cyclists out there, the same as there are bad motorists, but some of you need to lighten up and not be so fucking self-righteous. You are not all blameless.

Pubs

Where are all the old-school pubs disappearing to? They are slowly closing down and being boarded up and being put into extinction like the dinosaur. It is a crime. Recently I have seen one grand old pub turned into a Tesco Metro!

I love the original pub. It was THE place for men to gather and talk about sex, politics, religion, sport, and work. Saturday nights the ladies were allowed into this predominantly male environment, but other times it was mostly just men.

Great pub names stood the test of time. They were simple but strong: Kings Head, Rose and Crown, the Portcullis. Now what have we got... The Frog and Toad, The Slug and Lettuce, The Handbag and Scarf or whatever. Definitely not manly...

These days, 'pubs' are inhabited with hordes of screaming kids throwing tomato ketchup sachets around and spilling Coca-Cola and crisps everywhere. There are screaming babies in prams. Mothers breast-feeding them while sipping on a glass of wine. Women gather to drink coffee and eat muffins while hearing the latest gossip.

The menu boasts a hundred dishes from around the world. In my day it was a bag of 'Big D' peanuts, or pork scratchings. A packet of crisps if you were really hungry. Bar snacks ranged from a pork pie to a curled-up cheese sandwich. That was it. Pubs were a place to drink and play darts or pool or read a newspaper.

No forty inch flat-screen televisions blaring out so you can't hear yourself speak.

The pub toilet had a condom machine or Durex machine, as it was known, that sold just the said item. Now we have mints, headache tablets, fucking shoe polish, wine gums, cuddly toys and God knows what else.

I suppose looking at it, there is some sense in it all. Imagine you bought a packet of condoms believing your luck was in. You brought a lady back to your place and started kissing on the sofa, and she commented that your breath smelt of beer. You could whip out your mints and pop one in your mouth. Problem solved.

Or she complained she had a headache. You could magically produce your trusty packet of Anadin. No excuses now for when you go for the condoms. Sorted!

Pubs were a place of male refuge. Old guys could sit by the fire in peace and quiet with a pint and their paper without the fear of Debbie and Cheryl parking their lardy asses down next to them, and bitching about 'her across the street', or moaning about their breast implants.

Worse still, bellowing into their phone to 'our Gary!' Fucking frightening.

Where do all the old boys go now?

The face of the great British pub has changed forever. What a shame.

Well, I feel a whole lot better now for getting a few things off my chest. I could go on and on but maybe I will save that for another day and another book.

Summing up

Will we ever see the emergence of the real man again or will they have to live in secret, hiding their true feelings? Forever being confused and lost in the male/female wilderness...

If the apocalypse came tomorrow and in its aftermath man survived, I feel then we would see the rise of the real men once again. The hunter gatherer. The warrior. He would have to claim his natural birthright once more as the Lord Protector. Strong, tough, charismatic. A man ready to fight for his rights, his family, his survival.

A man that women would want to be around. They would feel safe in his presence. Comfort in his strong arms.

In this post-apocalypse era, how many of today's men would honestly survive?

How could they?

The majority have gone fucking soft. Lying in bed with man flu. Or debating over a cappuccino the merits of a Dyson vacuum over a Hoover.

How the fuck could these guys protect you and fight for a brave new world?

Women, while you have emasculated males around you, remember who you would want striding with purpose to save you in this dawn of destruction. A Gerald Butler or a Gok Wan?

When you need to find water, make fire and find food, would you want a Ray Mears at your side or an Ainsley Harriot?

When you have to be protected from hordes of mutants killers, do you want a Clint Eastwood figure fighting for you, or a Dale Winton?

If the dark times arrive, believe me, the real men, the so-called dinosaurs, will rule the Earth again.

Make no mistake. We are still out there, just waiting.

If the time comes, the colour pink will be a thing of the fucking past.

A great ritual burning of all things metrosexual will occur just like in the film the 'The Wicker Man'. Huge piles of gay clothes, manbags, hair gels and moisturers will go up in flames.

I shall rejoice and cheer that man has rediscovered himself and will rightly rule the world once more.

I hope you enjoyed my tongue in cheek journey through all things manly and you have not been traumatised too much. God knows in this day and edge we need a good laugh. Life can be grim at times. I hope this book has brought a smile to your face and brightened your day.

I don't believe all dinosaurs are not still wanted in this modern society, thence I believe the popularity of the Jurassic Park films. We still like to see them, hear them and quite rightly marvel at them.

We still have a place on this planet otherwise everything will have gone girly, gay, fluffy and pink. This cannot and will not happen.

I feel a good stiff drink and a viewing of the Magnum P.I. boxset is in order but I must first vacuum the lounge first and bake that quiche... like fuck!

See ya.

Clinton, Steele.

March 2013

APPENDIX

THINGS WE MISS ABOUT THE SEVENTIES

- Candy cigarettes
- Flying saucers (soda flavoured candy discs)
- Pop Rocks (You can still buy them!)
- Mood rings
- We called our aunts and uncles, 'Aunt' and 'Uncle', never their first names only
- Tupperware parties
- Double bill movies
- Local TV stations signing off at midnight with the national anthem
- Three channels on the TV
- No TV remote
- No microwave
- No central heating or air conditioning.
- Eating fast food was a treat you got maybe once a month
- Sodas were a treat that you got maybe two or three times a month
- Shag carpet
- Harvest Gold and Avocado Green Appliances
- Glasses and towels inside boxes of washing detergent
- Green Shield stamps
- Wooden console TVs
- TV dinners on TV trays in front of the TV
- Clackers (until they were banned)
- Skip Ball (ankle slips through a ring that has a bit of cord with a ball on the end. As you sling the ball around one ankle,

you jump over the cord and ball with the other foot. Great exercise!)

- Hoola-hoops
- Wearing a seatbelt in a car was not required
- Everything had a closing time, nothing stayed open 24 hours
- Most businesses that could were closed on Sundays
- Home phones were called landlines
- Petrol came in two, three or four star and it was cheap compared to today
- There was no "pay at the pump"
- Most places didn't accept credit cards, if you even had a credit card.
- No trick-or-treaters at Halloween
- No video games
- No cable or satellite TV
- Rotary dial phones
- We played outside all day, no matter how hot or cold it was
- No bicycle helmets or knee pads
- No bottled water
- You only got to watch cartoons on Saturday mornings
- Metal slinkies
- Suzy Bake oven and washing machine
- Banana seat bicycles
- Glass milk bottles
- Aztec chocolate bars
- Pony drink
- Joining the Tufty club
- No crap dance or R &B music
- Trains and buses that are on time and not overpriced
- No reality TV stars
- Parkinson chat show
- Red phone boxes

- Endless summers and basically proper seasons
- All the shops shut on a Sunday and sitting down with the family for Sunday dinner.
- MOST OF ALL THE SEVENTIES FULL STOP.